BOSPORUS BRIDGE

GW00775682

BOSPORUS BRIDGE

Design and construction

W. C. BROWN, M. F. PARSONS

and

H. S. G. KNOX

THE INSTITUTION OF CIVIL ENGINEERS, LONDON

CONTENTS

First published *Proc. Instn Civ. Engrs,* Part 1, 1975, 58, Nov., 505–557 ; 1976, 60, Aug., 503–530

Reprinted in this edition, 1976

ISBN 0 7277 0039 1

Made and printed in Great Britain by William Clowes & Sons, Limited
London, Beccles and Colchester

7855

BOSPORUS BRIDGE

Part I: History of design

W. C. BROWN, OBE, BSc, DIC, PhD, MICE*

M. F. PARSONS, BSc, FICE*

Part II: Construction of superstructure

H. S. G. KNOX, BSc, FICE†

The first part of the Paper describes the factors leading to the decision to construct a bridge across the Bosporus Straits in Istanbul. The various early proposals are outlined and the factors leading to the adoption of the present configuration are explained in detail. The construction was financed by international loans which are to be repaid by tolls levied on vehicles crossing the bridge, and a description of the electronic toll registration system is included.

The bridge was constructed in a record time for the size and type of structure. In the second part of the Paper the methods used in the manufacturing shops of several countries and on site in order to achieve this are explained. The Paper discusses how the problems set by the design, the local conditions and the financial background were overcome, and how new economies on construction were made. Emphasis is placed on changes in practice from those used on the generally similar Severn Bridge.

Ordinary Meeting, 5.30 pm, 13 January, 1976. Written discussion closes 30 January 1976, for publication in *Proceedings*, Part 1.
* Freeman Fox and Partners.
† Cleveland Bridge and Engineering Co. Ltd.
Proc. Instn Civ. Engrs, Part 1, 1975, **58**, Nov., 505-567

Part I: History of design

W. C. BROWN
M. F. PARSONS

Introduction

Modern Turkey, with its capital city of Ankara high on the central Anatolian plateau and its largest city and commercial centre of Istanbul situated on the NW shore of the Sea of Marmara in Thrace, is a country physically divided by the Bosporus. This narrow stretch of water links the Black Sea in the north with the Sea of Marmara in the south. Some 22 km long, it is just under 1 km wide at its narrowest point, broadening out occasionally into particularly picturesque bays (Fig. 1).

2. It was natural, however, that a permanent link should be contemplated: although a few tentative engineering solutions were proposed in the latter half of the 19th century, none could have received serious consideration. Thus it was not until the early 1950s when, with the development of intercity road communication within Turkey, the government gave serious consideration to the problem of crossing the Bosporus. A comprehensive traffic study was undertaken by De Leuw Cather in 1956, and its broad conclusion was that a permanent crossing was feasible and economically viable, the line selected being between the villages of Ortaköy on the west bank and Beylerbeyi in the east. This placed the crossing 4 km north of the point where the waters of the Bosporus and Golden Horn flow into the Sea of Marmara and where the straits are just over 1 km wide. At this location, as along most of the narrow section of the straits, the shores slope steeply and the water rapidly reaches a depth of over 50 m.

3. Although essentially a traffic study, the report not unexpectedly concluded that the most suitable form of bridge would be of the suspension type, but with its piers founded just within the straits, and it should be capable of carrying four lanes of highway traffic. A shipping width of 750 m and headroom of 50 m were considered adequate for all future water traffic (Fig. 2). The report was accepted by the government, and a suitable bridge design was commissioned and prepared by Messrs Steinman, Boynton, Gronquist and

Fig. 1
Map of Bosporus Straits

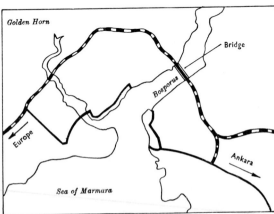

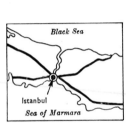

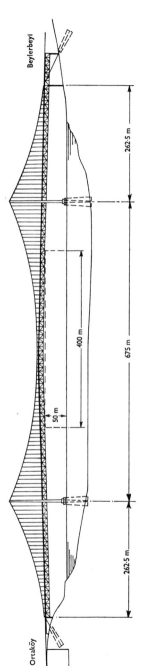

Fig. 2 Proposal by De Leuw Cather

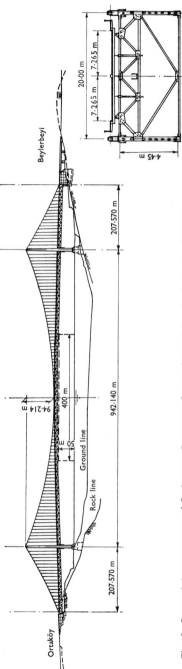

Fig. 3 General Arrangement of Steinman, Boynton, Gronquist and London's design (1960)

3

London of New York. This was duly completed and all documents were ready for international tendering by 1960. A general arrangement of this design is shown in Fig. 3. It is of classical form, with a central span of 942 m and headroom for shipping of 50 m, and carries four 3·5 m wide traffic lanes. It will be noted that both piers were to be founded in the water. Financing was to be arranged through USA sources and the construction cost was expected to be in the region of $40 million.

4. Unfortunately political unrest in Turkey during 1960 caused the project to be shelved. However, the development of intercity roadworks continued and national and international traffic volumes increased so rapidly that, although greatly improved, the vehicle ferries became increasingly unable to cope effectively with the volume of traffic. Long delays became commonplace, particularly during the summer months. Thus in 1967, after a very careful assessment of its economic priority within the overall national development, the Turkish government included the construction of the Bosporus Bridge in the highway construction programme of its forthcoming 5 year plan.

5. Prior to 1960 all existing major suspension bridges had been built in the USA, but with the completion of the Forth Road Bridge in 1964 and the Severn and Salazar Bridges in 1966 European engineers and contractors also possessed such necessary expertise. Thus when consideration of the Bosporus crossing was revived in 1967, European experience was available. Of significance also was the fact that by this time Turkey had become an associate member of the European Economic Community and thus the European Investment Bank was a ready source for outside financial aid.

6. Engineering proposals were therefore invited from consulting engineers in both the United States and Europe. Freeman Fox and Partners presented their preliminary proposals in October 1967, and a formal agreement was made with them by the Turkish government in January 1968. Speedy construction was of prime importance and it was hoped to invite tenders early in the following year. Apart from the preparation of the design and tender documents, however, international financing of the project remained to be arranged. The original programme envisaged completion in less than 4 years, including an allowance of 9 months for the collection of site data and for design. This was a short period for such a project but such was the public demand that every effort was to be devoted to its achievement. Previous design experience was of value and it was possible not only to introduce several innovations but to consolidate and adapt previous designs to suit the site conditions. The bridge is thus a design suited to its location (Fig. 4). The reasons leading to the adoption of specific features are explained later.

7. Not unnaturally, such an ambitious programme soon experienced delay, for although all tender documents were completed on schedule, negotiations with those nations prepared to participate in the financing syndicate took longer, and these were not sufficiently advanced for tenders to be invited from various international contracting consortia until June 1969.

8. Although the United States government had withdrawn from the financing syndicate, several American contracting companies with European bases were interested in tendering for the construction, and to broaden the interest, two designs had been prepared. The primary difference was in the suspended roadway platform. The preferred design used a 3 m deep streamlined shallow box girder, while the alternative incorporated an open lattice

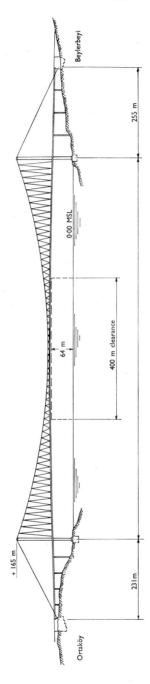

Fig. 4 General arrangement of bridge

girder truss 6 m deep integrated with a steel roadway deck and lower lateral bracing to provide torsional stiffness (Fig. 5). The alternative scheme was heavier and needed larger towers to sustain the greater wind forces, as well as requiring increases in cables and anchorages and a somewhat steeper road grade to maintain the shipping headroom, which had now been increased to 64 m. It was nevertheless felt that some contractor's greater experience and familiarity with this type of construction could offset the increased material cost and thus broaden the scope for competition in tendering.

9. In the event, however, there were no offers for this scheme and all tenders were based on the shallow box deck design. In September 1969 four groups returned tenders, three of the groups being formed from European companies and the remaining group from Japanese companies. Regrettably American companies withdrew their interest in the later stages. Each consortium nominated a leader company and the initial result of the tendering was:

	$
(a) Krupp/MAN/Redpath Dorman Long	36 505 000
(b) IHI/Julius Berger	36 431 000
(c) Beton und Monierbau/Sir Wm Arrol	36 408 000
(d) Hochtief/The Cleveland Bridge and Engineering Co.	35 083 000

10. Alternative proposals were not prohibited, and some groups offered alternative methods of construction or the use of alternative materials for the approach spans. The Anglo-German Bosporus Bridge consortium, for example, offered a significant reduction in cost by using the conventional in situ aerial cable wire placing system instead of preforming the wires in strands. After adjustments the revised tenders became:

	$
(a) Krupp/MAN/Redpath Dorman Long	35 665 000
(b) IHI/Julius Berger	36 031 000
(c) Beton und Monierbau/Sir Wm Arrol	35 427 000
(d) Hochtief/The Cleveland Bridge and Engineering Co.	33 721 000

11. It had been hoped to select the successful contractor quickly but unfortunately all offers contained some contractual and technical reservations, thus making a rapid decision more difficult. Almost all these reservations were either restatements of circumstances already covered by the conditions of contract or clear contraventions of the instructions to tenderers which the government could not accept. No acceptable basis for the award of the contract was therefore possible until all were unreservedly withdrawn. This caused further delay, and it was 4 months later before it was possible to sign the contract, some 2 months later than hoped. Only then could the financing agreements be finalized.

12. The final tender price, which included an agreement to make advance payments to the Contractor at the beginning of the construction period for repayment during the later stages, was $33 424 000, of which $21 775 000 was in foreign currency.

13. The ceremony inaugurating the works was held on 20 February, 1970, and the contractural starting date was fixed at 24 April, 1970. With a contract period of 1020 days, the completion date was therefore scheduled for 9 March, 1973.

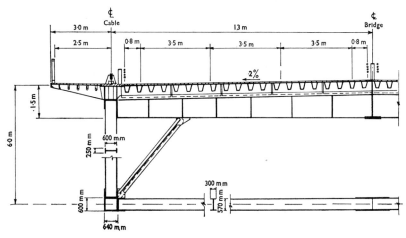

HALF CROSS SECTION MAIN SPAN

Fig. 5 Cross-section through Freeman Fox and Partners' truss bridge

Finance

14. In the interval between the preparation of the tender designs and the start of work on site, agreements were established with the financing nations and the European Investment Bank covering technical aspects of the project. Discussions with the engineering advisers and a board of consultants representing each of the funding nations, appointed by the Turkish government on the advice of the European Investment Bank, led to the general acceptance of the design. This was confirmed in an analytical check by Professor Dr-Ing. K. Klöppel of the Technische Hochschule, Darmstadt. Also during this period further site investigations had raised some doubts about the ground conditions at the west anchorage site. To satisfy all parties it was decided to increase the excavation at the rear of this anchorage and to carry out some in situ shear tests during the construction.

15. The engineering codes of the various countries providing financial support also differed and slight modifications were made to the tower sections to reduce the maximum local stress in sections 1 and 3, under the action of wind.

16. Loans were available as indicated in Table 1. Thus the financing

Table 1. Loans available from various sources

	US $ equivalent
Germany	7 500 000
France	3 750 000
Italy	1 875 000
Japan	22 500 000
United Kingdom	6 300 000
European Investment Bank	11 250 000

7

arrangements necessitated the placing of steelwork fabrication in several countries, and only after the placing of such contracts had been finalized could the tender design be rearranged to suit local manufacture, especially in the case of those steel sections required for stiffening the main tower and approach span plating. Such requirement was anticipated by the tender documents and alternative steels of comparable quality were accepted.

Factors leading to choice of tender design

17. Since the preparation of a design for a four lane bridge in 1960, further appraisal of likely traffic flows had indicated a probable need in the future for wider carriageways. After a study had estimated a first cost increase of 16% to extend the bridge from four to six lanes, a firm decision was made to prepare such a design. Investigations had also shown that potential shipping using the straits required an increase in headroom to 64 m over a central width of 400 m. Even before the bridge design started, its alignment had been settled by the line of the roads approaching it through the adjacent urban areas. The location of piers and anchorages remained to be settled by considerations of the engineering of the bridge itself.

18. Thus the first requirement was the establishment of the length of the central span. This was determined by an economic assessment of the variation in cost of towers, cable and anchorages as affected by the changes in cost of piers when placed on shore or in the water, including the risk element and associated reduction in overall construction time. It was shown that placing the piers on shore offered a distinct cost advantage, and since this also gave an unrestricted width for shipping, it was decided to adopt this configuration.

19. There was no difficulty locating the eastern pier just at the water's edge where the rock was near the surface, but conditions were different on the west. Here rock levels were much deeper, but much further movement inshore would have caused problems with traffic on the adjacent urban roadway, complicated the superstructure cable geometry and the erection of the end-suspended sections, and caused an increase in centre span. It was therefore decided to locate the west pier just between the urban roadway and the shore at a distance of 20 m from the latter, with an expected founding depth of around 18 m. The result of this study was the decision to place the piers on shore near the edge of the water and to make the centre span 1074 m long. Prior to start of construction, ground information for the southern part of the west pier was scanty since buildings had to be demolished before full investigations could be made.

20. The location of the east and west anchorage blocks presented little difficulty, natural topography, rock levels and boundary restraints imposed by the presence of the palace grounds at Beylerbeyi leaving little scope for alternative positioning.

21. Tunnel type anchorages were briefly considered, but proved to be uneconomic due to the presence of embankments at Beylerbeyi and the depth and condition of the rock at Ortaköy. Likewise a simple gravity type was unnecessary, so an excavated gravity form was adopted: in this type the strength and weight of the rock in front and at the sides of the anchorage are called upon in addition to the dead weight of the anchorage to resist the pull of the cables. Both anchorages take the form of a U in plan (Fig. 6), with the roof of the splay chambers forming the roadway.

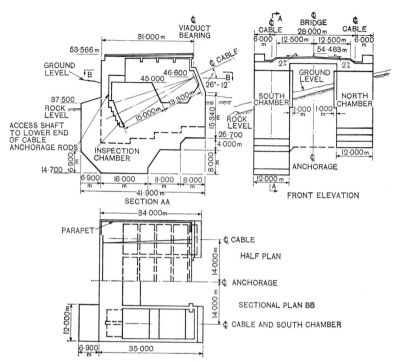

Fig. 6 Anchorages

22. It was clearly advantageous to make the cable entry into the chambers as low as possible, so as to reduce the overturning moment and hence the bearing pressures on the base. However, this could not be considered in isolation from the arrangements of the approach spans.

23. Whilst the classic form of suspension bridge has both its main and side spans suspended from the cable, such a configuration is by no means universal and each location has to be treated on its merits. In reality only the central span had to be suspended so that with banks sloping steeply from the shore and suitable foundation conditions close to the surface an alternative arrangement whereby the approach spans were independent presented itself. This arrangement was seen to have many advantages and to be more economical, the saving in construction cost being estimated at about $1·2 million. The potential saving in construction time was another important factor, an element which was given prominence during the preparation of the design. Other advantages resulting from not supporting the side spans from the cable were the elimination of problems associated with joining the cable to the anchorage at a low level, an increase in main span stiffness and the possibility of presetting the tower shorewards and so minimizing the bending stress induced by tower top movement.

24. The erection of a suspended box deck was straightforward over the water, where it could be hoisted directly, but erection over land presented

9

difficulty. This difficulty, however, would be avoided if the approaches were independently supported since they could be constructed at any time and in alternative forms without affecting the major suspension workings. Indeed, consideration was given to the use of prestressed concrete for the approach spans. At first sight this would have made possible a greater use of indigenous material and so a reduction in the amount of foreign finance. However, at that time experience with the material in Turkey was limited and thus any theoretical economy was unlikely to be realised. The question of source of finance was not an overriding requirement, especially as much of the local expenditure was likely to be covered by the convertible element of any foreign loan.

25. For the cables it was decided to use parallel wires for their greater efficiency rather than the alternative of preformed spiral strands. The alternative methods of forming parallel wire cable are either to adopt the aerial spinning system, whereby a few wires are carried across the span at one time, or to preform parallel wire strands with a socket at each end and to haul these across as a unit. Since the aerial spinning technique was available from only a few possible contracting companies, it was decided to design the saddles and cable attachments on the assumption that it would be built up from preformed parallel wire strands containing about 100 wires each. It was also considered that this system could be erected in less time than an aerial spun cable.

26. The use of concrete as an alternative material to steel in the towers was dismissed on account of the design problems associated with earthquake loading, as well as the belief that erection would take longer and thus result in overall higher costs.

Analysis and design
27. In general the analysis of this bridge structure follows that of the Forth Road Bridge[1] and the Severn Bridge[2], although for the Bosporus Bridge much greater use was made of computers.

Carriageway loading
28. The Turkish standard bridge loading is based on the American AASHO code, but increased by about 10% to convert short into metric tonnes. It was recognized that, whilst intended and acceptable for short to medium spans, some adjustment was necessary for application to longer spans. Thus, a modified BS 153 HA loading was adopted, together with the full 45 units of BS 153 HB. This was the first occasion on which a 180 t indivisible load was used for the design of any span in Turkey (previously the continental 100 t loading had been used for some special designs). Footway loading was similarly based on BS 153.

Wind
29. The bridge site is not exposed to particularly high winds, and those statistics which were available had not indicated maximum wind speeds in excess of 35 m/s; however, a somewhat higher speed of 45 m/s at deck level was used in the design for the calculation of static wind forces. The extrapolated wind speed at the tower tops was 51 m/s.

30. For erection loading, however, a uniform speed of 35 m/s was adopted in order to simplify calculations yet make allowance for the unlikely occurrence of the full design wind during short erection periods, when critical operation

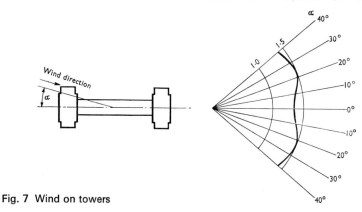

Fig. 7 Wind on towers

could if necessary be temporarily suspended. To have allowed for higher winds would have made an unnecessary addition to the cost of erection equipment. The wind forces on the suspended deck were obtained from static wind tunnel tests. These showed that, due to the streamlining, wind forces on the deck structure alone were equivalent to a flat plate of 32% of the girder depth. Wind loading on the cable and hangers was taken on an area equivalent to 0·6 times their respective diameters, with no reduction or shielding between the two lines.

31. However, a significant shielding factor was found to be present when a test was made on the tower legs. This shielding is clearly a function of wind incidence and the effect is shown in Fig. 7.

32. Conventional assessment of wind pressure in accordance with BS 153 was assumed all over the approach viaducts, where its influence on the design of the structure was slight. Model tests would no doubt have shown the design loading to be conservative, especially as the sloping deck configuration continued from the suspended span and would have introduced a streamlining effect to the wind drag forces.

Aerodynamic stability

33. To confirm the aerodynamic stability of the bridge, models of a length of the suspended deck were made and tested in a wind tunnel at the National Physical Laboratory, Teddington, England. The models were of rigid construction, made to a linear scale of 1:50, and represented a length of deck of approximately 100 m. In order to simulate the bending and torsional motions of the full-scale bridge the models were mounted on springs to allow vertical and pitching motions.

34. The physical properties of the full size bridge as given in Table 2 were used in determining the characteristics of the models and their mountings.

35. The models were tested for full-scale wind speeds of up to 58 m/s and for angles of inclination between $-5°$ and $+5°$ for both single degree of freedom motion and for coupled oscillation. Coupled oscillations, which were shown to be classical flutter instability, occurred at wind speeds well above the design maximum wind speed. The experimental critical wind speed at zero angle of inclination was 60 m/s.

11

Earthquake

36. The bridge was designed for basic horizontal and vertical seismic coefficients of 0·1 and 0·05 respectively, with modification factors corresponding to the predominant mode of vibration of each structural element, as recommended in a report commissioned by the Turkish government.[3]

37. Seismic motions parallel and transverse to the longitudinal axis of the bridge were both considered.

Table 2. Physical properties of Bosporus Bridge

Physical property	
Total mass of suspended structure, including cables (t/m)	15·0
Second moment of mass about longitudinal axis, including cables (tm²/m)	1600
Distance of centroid below top of deck at centre line (m)	0·90
Distance of neutral axis position below top of deck at centre line (m)	1·18
Lowest natural frequencies (Hz):	
symmetric bending	0·156
symmetric torsion	0·315
antisymmetric bending	0·117
antisymmetric torsion	0·430

Table 3. Combination of loads

Combination No.	Loading	Allowable stress factor
1	Dead load	1·0
2	HA live load and footway load Dead load HB vehicle 45 m/s wind Temperature ± 28°C	1·25
3	Dead load HA or HB live load and footway load 32 m/s wind Temperature ± 28°C	1·25
4	Dead load Earthquake ½ live load Temperature ± 28°C	1·33
5	Erection loads 45 m/s wind Temperature ± 28°C	1·25
6	Erection loads Earthquake Temperature ± 28°C	1·33
7	*Piers only* 1·5 × maximum overturning moment from combination 5 or 6	1·7
8	*Anchorages only* 1·5 × maximum cable pull from any of load combinations 1–6	1·7

Table 4. Allowable stresses in kg/mm²*

	Mild steel		High yield steel
Yield point	23·6	25·2	35·4
Tension on net area	14·2	15·0	20·8
Compression on tower plates	14·2	15·0	20·8
Compression on effective gross section for axially loaded struts:			
$l/r=$ 0	14·2	15·0	20·8
20	13·2	13·9	19·6
40	12·3	12·9	18·0
60	11·2	11·5	15·6
80	9·4	9·9	12·3
100	7·6	7·9	9·1
120	6·0	6·3	6·9
Bending in plates, flats and tubes	15·7	16·5	23·1
Bending in girders	15·0	15·8	21·9
	(d/t less than 85)		(d/t less than 75)
Bending in girders	14·2	15·0	20·8
	(d/t more than 85)		(d/t more than 75)
Maximum shear stress	10·2	11·0	15·4
Average shear stress	8·7	9·4	13·1
Bearing stress on flat surfaces	18·9		27·8
Direct stress in main cables	*Special quality steels*		
	70 kgf/mm²		
Maximum design load in hangers	50% of breaking load		
Friction value of 22 mm grip bolt per contact surface	6·5 tonnes		

Class	Concrete works cube strength	Compressive stresses		Shear stress	Average bond stress
		Direct	Bending		
A	4·4	1·21	1·61	0·092	0·105
B	3·2	0·88	1·17	0·092	0·105
C	2·1	0·57	0·76	0·070	0·085

	Tensile stress	Compressive stress
Mild steel reinforcement:		
up to 38 mm dia.	14·1	12·7
over 38 mm dia.	12·7	11·2

* Allowable stresses used for the main parts of the structure are based on ICE Civil Engineering Code of Practice no. 4, 1954; Foundations BS Codes of practice CP114, 1957, Reinforced concrete; CP115, 1959, Prestressed concrete; CP117, Part 2, 1967, Composite construction, and BS 153, part 3B, 1958, Steel girder bridges

Materials

38. The design was so arranged that all the main structural elements could be fabricated from normal commercial high yield or mild steel similar to BS 4360. The stresses in the lower flanges and webs of the shallow box girder permitted the use of mild steel, while elsewhere the higher grade was used. High grades of heat treated steels were used in the hanger pins and cable band bolts, as well as in the close tolerance and grip bolts used in the tower and approach spans.

39. The wire for the cable was similar to that commonly used on previous long span suspension bridges and was of high carbon manganese drawn to 5 mm dia. and coated with zinc by the hot dipped process, typical chemical composition being C, 0·8–0·85; Mn, 0·5–0·7; Si, 0·15–0·25. Ultimate and 0·2% proof stresses achieved were 160 kg/mm² and 115 kg/mm² respectively.

Stresses and loading

40. Loads and permitted steelwork stresses were generally in accordance with BS 153 and those adopted for the particular loading combination are shown in Tables 3–6.

41. The combinations of loading conditions which have been considered and the allowable stress factors are given in Table 3. In each case, each unit in the combination has been applied in the position and direction to cause the worst effect. For each combination, the maximum allowable design stress is the allowable stress factor multiplied by the basic allowable stress.

42. The dead load of the suspended structure used for design is as shown in Table 5.

Deck

43. The suspended roadway deck, although making a necessary contribution to the dead weight of the suspended span, does not provide any significant longitudinal bending resistance to traffic loading. Its purpose is to form a platform which spreads traffic loads to the hangers, and to be sufficiently

Table 5. Dead loads of bridge measured along horizontal (t/m)

	Main span	Ortaköy sidestay	Beylerbeyi sidestay
Cables	3·32	3·90	3·86
Cable wrapping	0·08	0·09	0·09
Cable bands	0·11	0·03	0·03
Handropes	0·02	0·02	0·02
Protective treatment	0·01	0·01	0·01
Hangers and sockets	0·16		
Suspended box steelwork	8·02		
Roadway surfacing	2·25		
Footway surfacing	0·08		
Parapets and crash barriers	0·20		
Services	0·22		
Protective treatment	0·07		
Total design dead load	14·54	4·05	4·01

Table 6. Maximum cable tensions at tower saddles (load in t/cable)

		Ortaköy Backstay	Main Span Cable	Beylerbeyi Backstay
(a) Dead load		12 800	11 948	12 650
(b) Live load Case 1 (whole span loaded)	Bending	2 020	1 892	1 996
Live load Case 1 (whole span loaded)	Torque	239	220	236
(c) Temperature (−28°C)		153	134	150
45 m/s longitudinal wind on unloaded main span		140	50	140
32 m/s longitudinal wind on unloaded main span		70	25	70
32 m/s longitudinal wind on live load case 1		70	33	70
Longitudinal earthquake		222	85	217
Total cable tension for combination 1		15 059	14 060	14 882
Total cable tension for combination 2		13 093	12 132	12 940
Total cable tension for combination 3		15 352	14 252	15 172
Total cable tension for combination 4	Case A (Longitudinal earthquake)	14 304	13 223	14 133
Total cable tension for combination 5	Case B (Transverse earthquake)	14 082	13 138	13 916
Total design axial stress in cable for combination 1 f_t kgf/mm² $F_t = 70·0$ kgf/mm²		68·8	68·5	

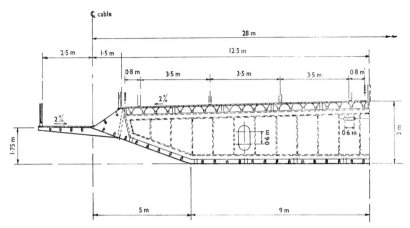

Fig. 8 Cross-section through deck

rigid in torsion to make a major contribution to the overall aerodynamic stability. Within these limitations the deck was made as light, and therefore as shallow, as practicable. A depth of 3 m at the centre line was found to be adequate.

44. The chosen depth is suitable for the use of plated diaphragms. A deeper section would have required plate widths beyond those easily available, or additional butt welds. The cross-section is shown in Fig. 8.

45. The upper deck plates are 12 mm thick and these span 300 mm transversely between the V shaped, 6 mm thick, pressed trough members, which in turn span between the diaphragms spaced 4475 mm apart. The V troughs are, however, continuous through the diaphragm plates which represents a departure from the Severn Bridge arrangement. In that design, trough ends were butted at the diaphragm and this required care in the fabrication, particularly in the site assembly techniques. Another variation was the change from U to V troughs. This was primarily to ease the production of such elements in long lengths but also had the effect of slightly increasing stiffness. Single-sided bulb flat stiffening sections were used elsewhere in the deck section. These were attached by reeled intermittent fillet welds, and the resulting welding stresses as measured by plate shrinkage were minimized. All trough welds were continuous.

46. The span was divided into 60 units, each 17 900 mm long. Each unit was made up of 22 stiffened plate elements from five basic types, with maximum weight of 8·5 t and width of 3500 m. Thus much repetition was introduced, permitting the use of fabrication jigs with subsequent improvement in dimensional accuracy. A particular feature of the design was that no special tolerance in dimension was necessary. Any variation in the overall sizes of jig-fabricated plate elements was clearly well within site assembly adjustment or could be accommodated without difficulty. The overall width of any section was not important provided it matched the adjacent unit and slight staggering of the transverse splice was easily accommodated. An introduction

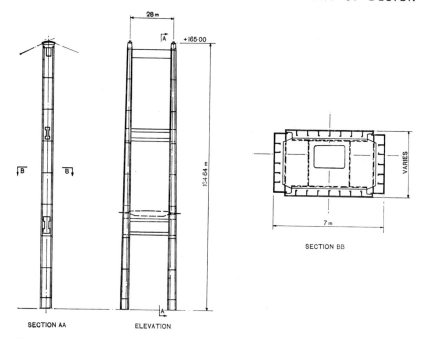

Fig. 9 Towers

of unnecessary tolerances would only have led to further expense and confusion.

47. The 38 mm thick mastic asphalt roadway surfacing is similar to that used for the Severn Bridge and was applied directly by hand methods to the zinc sprayed upper plating. Although not perfect, such surfacing represents the best currently available.

Towers

48. The towers (Fig. 9) follow the design used for the Severn Bridge, but with adjustments to suit the increased span and carriageway widths. A short base section was introduced incorporating mild steel, and this made the attachment of shear connectors and holding down brackets more convenient. Such means of transfer of load from the steel tower to the concrete pier was necessary to provide a clear area at the tower base for the access of the public lifts, each taking 18 passengers, which were to be installed. These base sections were clearly special, but by bringing them a further 6500 mm above the pier tops, the tower length could be conveniently divided into eight similar sections each 19 500 mm long—a length convenient for fabrication (Fig. 10).

49. High yield steel was used for all the main plating and stiffening, but to keep problems associated with its welding to a minimum, plate thicknesses

were held at a maximum of 22 mm and plates of either this width or 20 mm were used throughout. Single-sided bulb flats were used as stiffeners, with transverse stiffeners and diaphragms at suitable centres.

50. Sections to British rollings were indicated on the tender design, but it was realized that these were provisional and in fact they were later changed to Italian sizes once it was decided to place the fabrication work there.

51. From the adoption of a single box section and the use of plates of 22 mm maximum thickness came the dimensions and width of the side panels. These are 5600 mm wide, and it was clear therefore could not be transported freely. However, to have reduced their width would have involved such considerable extra effort in fabrication and erection as to more than offset any inconvenience in transportation.

52. The ends of all panels were carefully milled so that all compression loads are carried directly. Tensile forces arising during the free standing erection stage were carried by high tensile screwed rods, pretensioned to prevent the joint opening under expected wind pressures. Apart from close tolerance locating bolts at the ends of each panel, all the shear forces are carried by waisted grip bolts (22 mm dia.) fitting in 24 mm dia. holes.

53. In determining the stress in the tower plating, it was assumed that there would be a tower top positional error of 150 mm and likewise that fabrication would be of good commercial standards. Cold mangling of all plates was specified and jig assembly was required. Intermittent welding was used to keep weld stresses and shrinkage to the same order as in conventional rolled sections. Thus no special allowance to take account of fabrication irregularity was necessary beyond the usual accepted factors. The critical stresses of the stiffened panels were in excess of 2·5 times the maximum calculated stress.

Cables

54. The cables are built up from parallel wire, 5 mm in diameter over the hot dipped galvanizing. The steel has a 0·2% proof stress of 120 kg/m and a minimum ultimate strength of 160 kg/mm². The tension in the cables varies along their length, becoming a maximum at the landward side of the tower. Because of the change in inclination of the cable, the tension is different on either side of the saddle; this difference is normally sustained by frictional resistance between the cable wire and the tower saddle and is somewhat greater than with most previous bridges. In order to reduce this friction and to save cable wire in the main span, a proportion of the wires was anchored off at each tower. The main span cable contains 10 414 wires, each 5 mm in diameter, while both side spans have 11 176 wires.

55. The tender design envisaged 82 preformed parallel wire strands, each containing 127 wires, with a weight not exceeding 50 t. In the final arrangement, however, the number of strands was reduced to 19, each having 448 wires, with another four strands, each of 192 wires, in the backstays. Their arrangement and that of the anchor devices at the tower tops is shown in Figs 11 and 12.

Foundations

56. On the European side at Ortaköy, the towers, anchorages and viaduct foundations all rest on contorted mudstone or schistose rocks of Upper

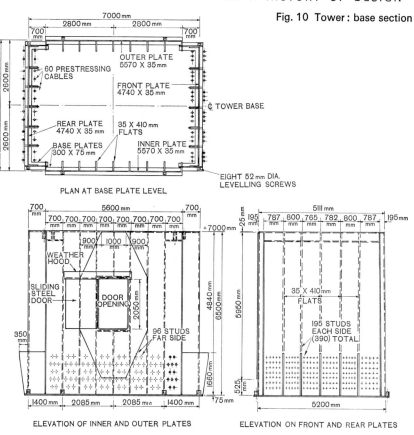

Fig. 10 Tower: base section

60 PRESTRESSING CABLES

OUTER PLATE 5570 X 35 mm

FRONT PLATE 4740 X 35 mm

℄ TOWER BASE

REAR PLATE 4740 X 35 mm

35 X 410 mm FLATS

BASE PLATES 300 X 75 mm

INNER PLATE 5570 X 35 mm

PLAN AT BASE PLATE LEVEL

EIGHT 52 mm DIA. LEVELLING SCREWS

WEATHER HOOD

SLIDING STEEL DOOR

DOOR OPENING

96 STUDS FAR SIDE

ELEVATION OF INNER AND OUTER PLATES

35 X 410 mm FLATS

195 STUDS EACH SIDE (390) TOTAL

ELEVATION ON FRONT AND REAR PLATES

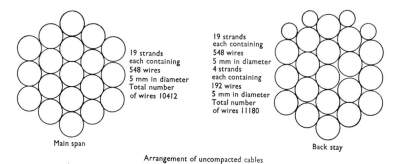

19 strands each containing 548 wires 5 mm in diameter Total number of wires 10412

19 strands each containing 548 wires 5 mm in diameter 4 strands each containing 192 wires 5 mm in diameter Total number of wires 11180

Main span

Back stay

Arrangement of uncompacted cables

Fig. 11 Strand arrangement

19

Fig. 12 Strand anchorage

Devonian age. The strata were folded during subsequent mountain building periods so that their orientation changes rapidly within a few metres. On the Asian side, at Beylerbeyi, the bedrock is mainly of limestone with some schist layers occurring in the pier foundations.

57. The ground level at the site of each tower is about 3 m above sea level and the concrete piers extend down to sound bedrock, each tower leg being fixed on a separate pier. On the Ortaköy side, the pier bases are 17 and 24 m below sea level, and on the Beylerbeyi side 5 and 10 m below sea level. The main tower foundations at Beylerbeyi are rectangular in plan (15 m × 19 m), but at Ortaköy the foundation excavations are circular and 18 m in diameter.

58. The original subsoil investigations had been carried out while the

20

area above the south cofferdam was still built up, and the early boreholes had been put down around the perimeter of the area. The preliminary designs for the foundation were based on these surveys, with the proviso that amendment might be required when the ground was opened. When the site was eventually cleared, new borings indicated that the south cofferdam would have to be taken to a depth of at least 22 m.

59. Although the piers on both sides are sited close to the water's edge, removal of water entering the excavations required only limited pumping (Fig. 13).

Approach spans

60. The side spans are steel/concrete composite structures, independent of the cable, and are 231 and 255 m long on the Ortaköy and Beylerbeyi sides respectively. Mild steel is used throughout for the shorter west spans, but high yield steel is used in all the box girders of the eastern shore, the longer spans on the latter being determined largely by the need to keep the piers to a mini-

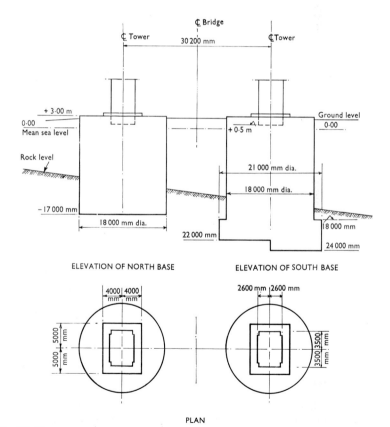

ELEVATION OF NORTH BASE   ELEVATION OF SOUTH BASE

PLAN

Fig. 13 Piers

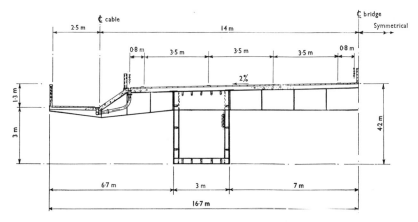

Fig. 14 Approach spans: cross section through roadway

mum within the garden of the old palace over which the bridge passes.   Fig. 14 shows a cross-section through the roadway, which uses a 200 mm reinforced concrete slab supported at 3000 mm centres by transverse cross-beams framing into the box girders, spaced laterally at 17 m centres.   All spans are continuous and anchored to the main cable anchorages, to which all longitudinal forces are transferred.

61.   Lateral forces are carried to the tower and anchorage via the deck slab, the slender steel circular columns being free to accommodate movements in both directions either by pivotting or flexure.   The box girders are designed on conventional lines and in accordance with BS 153.

Toll collection system and bridge services

62.   To repay the loan and provide funds for the running costs of the bridge, tolls are collected from the vehicles passing over it.   There are 16 toll lanes, the central four being reversible for tidal flow traffic but with separate toll collecting equipment within the booths for each direction of traffic.

63.   It was realized that to cope with the intensive traffic flow and wide range of vehicles which would use the bridge, a toll registration system of advanced form would be required and would need to incorporate high security and rapid processing of vehicles combined with an instant audit facility. Experience has shown that with the common toll for a private car of 10 Turkish lira, which is invariably paid by note, toll collectors have been able to achieve rates of processing of between 700 and 800 vehicles for short periods.

64.   To allow easy recognition and manual classification of vehicles, and at the same time to enable the revenue to be maximized by paying regard to the large proportion of heavy vehicles of various types using the bridge, the tariff structure is based upon vehicle axles and easily recognizable types of vehicle. The tariff is divided into nine paying classes of vehicle, for each of which an additional toll can be levied for additional axles above a basic classification. A tariff adjusting factor can also be applied for special circumstances.

65.   The toll recorder automatically issues a printed record of the collector's transactions at the end of his shift: various other forms of printed record are provided automatically, including a daily record of vehicles by lane and by total for each direction of traffic and a traffic density record arranged to give a direct visual impression of the relative traffic densities in each hour throughout a 24 h period.

66.   Each collector is issued with a punched identity card and at the start of his shift he inserts this into a card reader in the collector desk before opening the lane to traffic.   The information on his identity card is automatically recorded by the toll recording equipment, for use in identifying the printed record of the shift.   As each vehicle stops at the booth, the collector registers the tariff class of the vehicle on a keyboard whereupon the toll charge is immediately displayed to the driver and to the collector.

67.   The driver's toll information is displayed on an indicator fitted on the side of the booth which also shows that the toll has been registered and the transaction completed by displaying a method of payment, i.e. by cash or by voucher (Fig. 15).   The class of vehicle is also displayed on large matrix signs mounted on the canopy above the lane and at a tolls monitor on the desk of an inspector situated in the administration building overlooking the whole toll area.   The classification signs on the canopy are angled towards the inspector's windows so that he can easily see them and identify them with the particular lane and any vehicle seen coming from or going into the lane.

68.   The toll recorder incorporates two data processors working in parallel as 'active' and 'passive' units.   Security of operation is further enhanced by using a processor monitor which determines by regular checks or output that

Fig. 15 Toll booth

the processors are in agreement and correct. In the event of a fault being detected in the 'active' unit, the monitor automatically changes the 'passive' unit to 'active' and warns the inspector. This changeover does not disturb the functioning of the toll system. The toll recorder is energized via battery type no-break equipment and an inverter to avoid incorrect functioning due to transient and long-term disturbances in the electric power supply.

69. All toll recording and operating sequences are preprogrammed on punched tape, separate tapes being prepared for operating sequences and tariff charges. All records are printed in plain language by teletyper machines instructed from the 'active' data processor. The teletypers may also be instructed to produce the information on punched tape in teletyper code so that further printed records can be obtained later.

70. Vehicle axles are counted by pneumatic pads arranged in patterns of four pads at each counting position. The data processors analyse the signals from the pads and compare them with the collector registration. A faulty pad detected at this stage is then automatically monitored to see whether the fault is consistent, and in this event the inspector is automatically warned.

71. Although this is not in use at present, the system incorporates provision for the collection of tolls at higher and lower tariff levels during certain hours. A master clock and programme controller will operate this facility, which can be preset to give independent periods of change of tariff for each direction of traffic.

72. The lanes are opened and closed manually at the start and completion of a shift by barriers in the form of posts which are raised from within the cable tunnel beneath the lanes. The posts are coloured amber and illuminated by internal fluorescent lamps which are automatically switched on as the post is raised. The inspector receives an indication if a lane is closed and the barrier left open. The line of toll booths is laid out in echelon across the toll plaza to improve the inspector's view of the booths and classification signs, and the windows of the inspector's room are angled to minimize reflexion (Fig. 16).

73. Traffic routing through the lanes is controlled by 300 mm conventional red and green traffic lights, mounted on the face of the canopy over each lane and interlocked with the lane opening and closing switches at the collector's desk. Red traffic lights are also left permanently energized to indicate that there is no way through a lane from a particular direction. A direct speech type of communication set is provided between the collector and the inspector, and a foot operated security alarm is provided for the collector.

74. A low light level, closed circuit television (CCTV) camera, with pan and tilt mountings, is fitted at each tower for general surveillance of the bridge. The CCTV monitors are placed above the inspector's desk and the cameras are remotely controlled by him. Communication between the inspector and the various bridge vehicles and maintenance and painting gangs is provided by VHF radio.

75. Emergency telephones for public use are placed at intervals along both sides of the bridge and provide communication with the inspector. Each phone is weatherproof and housed in a bright orange open-fronted glass fibre case with a clear telephone motif mounted on three sides.

76. The central control and surveillance point for day-to-day bridge operation is the inspector's room, which has a comprehensive control desk containing public telephones, communications and loud address to bridge

Fig. 16 Toll plaza

Fig. 17 Inspector's room

staff, toll monitoring panels and various general plant controls and indications, such as lighting, tower lifts, mains and standby generator power etc. The control faces of the desk are constructed from a tile matrix which provides flexibility in laying out such controls and general uniformity in appearance, being easily adapted to the various components mounted on the desk (Fig. 17).

25

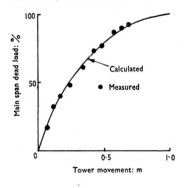

Fig. 18 (left) Tower deflexions

Fig. 19 (below) Measurements on tower plating

Fig. 20 (right) Bridge loading

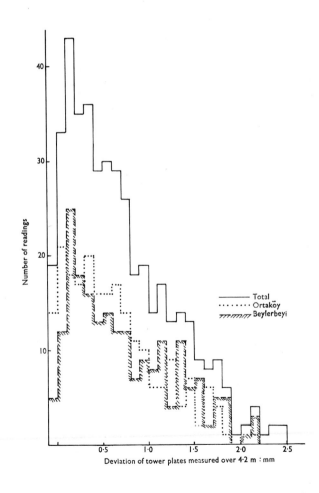

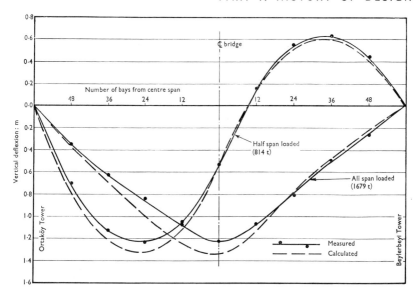

Checks on design assumptions

77.   During the course of the superstructure construction, measurements of the deflexion of the tower top were taken for comparison with the calculated values.   Fig. 18 shows the results obtained during the erection of the main span box girders and it will be seen that the actual and computed values were quite close.   Much depends on the accuracy with which the cable temperature can be measured, but clearly any final error in positioning of the saddle was small and within the 150 mm allowance.

78.   Upon the publication of the Merrison Rules for box girders, a comparison was made between values of plate deformation contained therein and typical results obtained in practice using the particular method of fabrication and control adopted for this bridge.   A series of measurements made on the tower plating are shown in Fig. 19.   Other factors worth noting are that offsets of all such measurements were towards the bulb of the stiffener and that measurement of the plating rarely produced a deviation from plane of more than 1 mm over 700 mm and was always inward.   On no occasion was the deviation found to be antisymmetric between adjacent stiffeners.

79.   Measurements on the approach span box flanges produced similar results and confirmed that all deviations were well within 3 mm when measured over a 3 m length.   Tests on preformed model girders, and all previous experience, proved the adequacy of the design assumptions.   All engineers associated with the project and the financial sponsors were completely satisfied.

80.   In mid-October 1973 just before opening the bridge to traffic, two lanes of the south carriageway and the centre section of the north carriageway were loaded with a typical mixture of trucks amounting to a total load of 1679 tonnes.   The deflexions were measured and compared with calculated values.   The results are shown in Fig. 20.

BROWN, PARSONS AND KNOX

Progress

81. The bridge was substantially complete and available to carry public traffic by 15 August, 1973, some 160 days beyond the original date of 9 March, 1973. There is no doubt that the original programme, whilst not unreasonable, was ambitious and required good fortune and few unexpected difficulties. In the event, differences in the ground conditions at the Ortaköy and Beylerbeyi pier foundations, concurrent with design changes and protracted delivery of some erection equipment, prevented the scheduled start on the towers. This lost time was never recovered, so this and necessary last minute changes to some of the viaduct and main span lifting gear accounted for most of the delay.

Quantities of material

82. The quantities of material used in the construction of the bridge were as follows:

	t
Steel in main cables	5450
Steel in towers	4790
Steel in suspended deck	8710
Steel in approach spans	2950

The final cost of the bridge was $36 100 000

Acknowledgements

83. The Authors wish to acknowledge the contribution to the work made by the Turkish Ministry of Works, General Directorate of Highways, and in particular Servet Bayramoglu, General Director of Highways until November 1969; Atalay Coskunoglu, General Director from December 1969; Cahit Yalgin, Deputy Director of Highways; Ziya Cakmak, Bridge Director; M. Ali Terim, Chief Bridge Engineer; Muammer Tuglu, Assistant Chief Bridge Engineer; O. Saffettin Sile, Divisional Director; N. Akgun, Bosporus Bridge Director; and N. Oylu, Assistant Bosporus Bridge Director.

84. The Board of Consultants' members, appointed by the financing syndicate, were Professor Dr-Ing., E. H. K. Klöppel (Germany); Professor G. Oberti (Italy); Ing. M. Huet (France); Professor Dr A. Hirai (Japan); and J. F. Pain, (UK). The European Investment Bank Adviser was Jacques Faudon, and special advisers on foundations from the Royal School of Mines were Professor E. Hoek, Dr J. M. Boyd, Dr H. Kutter, Dr J. W. Bray and Dr T. R. Harper.

85. The staff of the Turkish firm of Petek which was concerned with the bridge were, on the design and contract preparation, Professor S. Kuran, O. Kuran and F. Keskinel, and on site supervision, Messrs Y. Gelgin, Y. Bayraktar, M. Kosebay, I. Onaral, T. Kilic and I. Karca. Staff of Freeman Fox and Partners are given in Appendix 1.

Part II: Construction of superstructure

H. S. G. KNOX

Introduction

The invitation to tender and associated contract documents for the Bosporus Bridge contained three features, apart from the design for the finished bridge described in Part I, which had a major effect on the methods adopted to carry out the contract. These were the programme, some factors which led to the submission and acceptance of an alternative tender, and the financial conditions.

87. The Bosporus Bridge was to be the fourth longest span suspension bridge in the world, and the longest in Europe. It would be an 'overseas' project for any likely contractor. Nevertheless, the tender invitation required that it should be built in a period of about three years, compared with between $3\frac{1}{2}$ years and almost 6 years for previous bridges of this size in the USA or the UK.

88. Some of this saving in time was, of course, due to the relatively easier pier and anchorage construction. This meant, however, that the early fabrication and the very large amount of engineering, design and manufacture of special equipment required for a major suspension bridge, had to be achieved in about one year less than is usually available (and needed). It was also true that river conditions placed fewer limitations on deck lifting operations than on the Severn, for example, but to take advantage of this required accelerating the deck assembly and many other operations much beyond what had been achieved on that job.

89. A comparison between the overall programmes achieved at Severn and Bosporus is shown in Fig. 21.

90. In the official tender design the method of construction of the main cables was specified. This was to be by the use of shop-prefabricated parallel wire strands, 127 wires to each strand and 1690 m long (plus additional back-stay strands). The Author's company realized that a very substantial saving in cost could be achieved by constructing the cables, of identical final form, by conventional aerial cable spinning. They were also confident that this would give much less risk of serious problems or delay in execution. Up to that time, there had been only one example of the use of prefabricated parallel-wire strands; that had been on a much smaller scale than proposed for Bosporus and was understood to have been attended by some problems.[4]

91. As the cable construction method formed part of the contract specification, cable spinning could only be offered by using the procedure for 'alternative designs'; this meant that a tender to the official design must also be submitted, and the alternative might not be considered. Both methods were priced and the tender based on cable spinning turned out to be about $1 670 000 cheaper than for the prefabricated strands, which tender was itself substantially below those of all competitors. The alternative tender was accepted and became the basis of the contract.

92. The only significant redesign of the permanent structure, required to

29

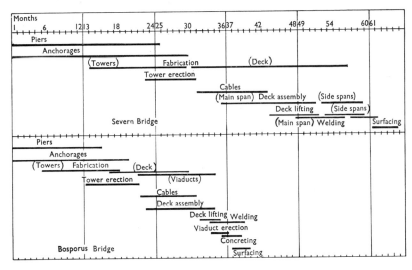

Fig. 21 Comparative actual programmes

allow cable spinning, was to the anchorages. This redesign was undertaken by the tenderer and took the form of a prestressed anchorage similar to that used for the Forth Road and Severn bridges, but using this time 40 mm Macalloy bars to prestress the slabs carrying the strand shoes to the concrete anchor face and to transmit the cable loads to the rear of the anchorage concrete. The bars were about 15·5 m long and were in single lengths without couplers. No changes were needed to the concrete dimensions, except for the different number and size of the ducts through it.

93. The effect of the financing arrangements for the project had a considerable bearing on the materials used and the manufacturing techniques. Each national loan had to be spent in the lender country and expenditure in that country had to be limited to the value of the loan. Tenderers had to declare with their tender the proportions of the various foreign currencies which they required, and these had to be considered as virtually fixed thereafter.

94. With the possible exception of Japan, none of the loans was large enough for the entire off-site work to be carried out in one country. Tenders therefore had to be based on multi-national consortia or on sub-contracting. The basis of the successful tender was a consortium of two partners only: one, Hochtief AG, fully responsible for the entire substructure and the viaduct concrete deck slabs, and the other, Cleveland Bridge, fully responsible for the entire steel superstructure but using sub-contractors in other countries to spread the supplies, as required for financial and capacity reasons.

95. After providing for overheads and margin, the large amount of special equipment necessary and some orders for minor permanent materials, the balance of the UK loan would permit only a small proportion of the major supplies to come from Britain. The substructure partner was utilising a major part of the money which could be spent in Germany. Therefore, for

reasons of available finance, from an assessment of technical ability and capacity, and having regard to commitments of parts of the relevant European industry in competing groups, Cleveland elected to base its tender on non-British supplies coming mainly from Italy, with the balance from Germany.

96. After some interchanges in the immediate post tender period, the final arrangement of major permanent supplies was that Italy supplied the towers, part of the suspended structure and the approach viaducts (totalling 10 840 t), and the UK supplied a further part of the suspended structure (5650 t), the suspenders, the cable band and splay castings, the anchorage steelwork, and Macalloy bars for anchorage prestressing. From Germany came the main cable and wrapping wire (5560 t), high strength grip bolts, close tolerance bolts and high tensile screwed rods. Later one sub-contract for the surfacing was placed in the UK, and other nominated sub-contracts for the bridge services in Germany and France, as well as Turkey. Details of the various suppliers are given in Appendix 2.

Supply
Principal materials
97. For rolled structural steels, the contract specified materials to BS 4360, mild steel being of grade 43A and high yield steel of grade 50B for the towers,

Table 7.

UNI 5334/5 grade	Properties	Comparison with BS grade
Mild steel: FE42B, with higher yields Min. tensile strengths	42 kg/mm²	43A 44·1
Yield strength, plates	to 19 mm: 25·2 kg/mm² 19–40 mm: 24·4 kg/mm²	25·2 24·4
Yield strength, sections	to 16 mm: 26·0 kg/mm² 16–25 mm: 25·0 kg/mm² 25–40 mm: 25·0 kg/mm²	26·0 25·2 24·4
Impact properties	3·5 kgm/cm² at ambient	none
High yield steel: FE52, with $C_p \div 0.23\%$ Min. tensile strength	52 kg/mm²	50 with $C_p \div 0.23\%$ 50·4
Yield strength	to 16 mm: 36·0 kg/mm² 16–30 mm: 35·0 kg/mm²	36·2 35·4
Sub-grades: (a) Tower plates: FE52C Impact properties (b) Tower sections: FE52B Impact properties (c) Deck and viaduct plates: FE52D Impact properties	3·5 kgm/cm² at 0°C 3·5 kgm/cm² at ambient 3·5 kgm/cm² at −20°C including 6 mm	50B none 50B none 50C 5·0 at −5° 3·5 at −15° over 6 mm
(d) Viaduct sections: FE52C Impact properties	3·5 kgm/cm² at 0°C	50C 3·5 at 0°

31

and 50C for the deck and viaducts. For high yield steels, there was an additional requirement that the carbon content on product analysis should not exceed 0·23%. Equivalents from alternative national standards were permitted. As the British grades were not exact equivalents of those in general European practice, much consideration had to be given to the steels to be used in Italy for the majority of the fabrication, and some orders on the mills there had to be non-standard.

98. Generally, grades from UNI5334/5 with slightly superior properties to the specified British grades were offered and used, in order to ensure quick approval. These were as given in Table 7 (with comparisons to specified BS 4360 grades).

99. The FE52 steels were produced by the basic oxygen and electric arc processes for plates, the basic oxygen process for bulb flats and open hearth for heavy angles. All were fully silicon-killed; niobium was not incorporated; FE52D plates were aluminium refined. All FE52 plates, including those below 12 mm thick, were normalized or controlled-rolled. The specified physical properties were readily achieved and the plate carbon contents for the high yield steel were comfortably below the specified limit. Rejects at the mills were insignificant. The surface finish was good and further flattening in the fabricating shops was not found necessary.

100. Steels for use in the British fabrication were, of course, supplied to the specified BS grades (with the carbon limitation where applicable).

101. For the main cable wire, the only specification for chemical analysis of the steel was that the phosphorus and sulphur contents should each not exceed 0·050%. The steel used to obtain the desired mechanical properties for the finished wire had a typical composition of C, 0·80%; Si, 0·21%; Mg, 0·52%; P less than 0·021%; S less than 0·029%. The wire drawing, galvanizing and the finished properties are described in §§ 117 and 118.

102. For protective treatment, the paints for the external surfaces (etch primer, phenolic zinc chromate and phenolic micaceous iron oxide) were manufactured in the UK, for the fabrication in Italy as well as for that in the UK. It was not practicable in the time available to carry out the necessary experiments and testing to prove equivalence of paints manufactured in Italy, where the specified types were not generally used.

103. For the internal surfaces, the contract specification required red lead to BS 2523 Type C and this was used for the UK fabrication. As the use of this paint was prohibited by Italian safety regulations, due to the white lead content, locally manufactured red lead equivalent to BS Type B was approved as an alternative. It is notable that the Type B paint appeared to stand up much better to sea transport and subsequent site exposure than the Type C.

104. For the surfacing by hand-laid mastic asphalt, attempts were made to locate stone in Turkey equivalent to the specified 6–9 mm cubical granite course aggregate and for the 13 mm angular chippings (with polished stone co-efficient of under 0·6) for use as precoated top dressing. These efforts were not successful and all the ingredients for the surfacing had to be shipped from the UK, using particular stones which had been successful on similar bridge applications in the UK.

Tower fabrication
105. Two factors severely limited the number of fabricating shops, in all

the eligible countries, which could make the towers. These were the very large panel sizes (typically 19·5 m long by 5·6 m wide) and the requirements for complete shop trial assembly. Many otherwise suitable shops including that of the Author's Company, were ruled out because it was impossible to transport the panels from the shop to a port or because they were unable or unwilling to make available the space required (under adequate cranage) for the assembly. To meet the original programme it was necessary for the two towers to be fabricated and assembled simultaneously. This made it virtually essential for their supply to be divided between two works. To deal with the transport problem, consideration was given to splitting the panels longitudinally, with additional site bolted joints, but the Engineer did not feel able to approve this. In the event, the Ortaköy Tower was made under the control of a northern Italian company in a works about 20 km from Palermo, Sicily, to which it was linked by a motorway with tunnels which were wide enough. The Beylerbeyi Tower was made in a works about 15 km from the port of Livorno. Here, road transport was quite impossible. The panels and the later viaduct boxes from the same works were transported to the port by rail, after modifications to the lineside structures and under special working.

106. In the details of fabrication methods it is of interest to note the different techniques used by the two works to achieve the required output and the same exacting results in dimensional accuracy and welding quality.

107. Plating and welding of individual panels was done in variants of the usual jig methods. Preparation of plates and other components was generally by high quality gas cutting. Mechanical edge planing was used only for the unwelded edges of high yield steel items, and as particularly noted in § 108.

108. For the Ortaköy Tower, all plating and tacking and most welding was carried out in the jigs. The butt welds joining the two or three pieces of the main external plates were made by one run only from each side, using the submerged arc process, on a preparation with no gap and nominal bevels only. Only the run from one side was made initially. The transverse stiffeners were then tacked to act as templates for positioning of the longitudinal bulb flats. The toes of the latter were edge planed. The 8 mm intermittent fillet weld joining the bulb flats to the plates was carried out in a single run with the panel remaining in the horizontal position. After adding the end plates and other minor components and tacking the side plates or corner angles, the panel was removed from the jig and turned over for these last to be finally welded and for the second run of the plate butt welds.

109. For the Beylerbeyi Tower panels, the run from one side for the similar plate butt welds was made outside the plating jigs. In these all longitudinal bulb flats were first set out and tacked, followed by tacking and welding of the transverse stiffeners, end plates and the side plates or corner angles. The panel was then removed from the jigs and placed in a tilting stand, to allow welding of the fillets between the bulb flats and plates in the gravity position, without the bulb flats having been edge planned. The panel was turned over to complete the butt and corner welds.

110. For the vertical seam bolt holes between the corner angles of the side panels and the side plates of the front and rear panels, consideration was initially given to various schemes for drilling a substantial proportion full size, either in preparation or on the fabricated panels before or after rather than during the shop assembly. In the event it was generally found preferable to

sub-drill holes in the preparation stage and ream full size during the shop assembly. For the Ortaköy Tower, the marking and sub-drilling of the corner angles was not done until after the end plate machining of the fabricated panels.

111. The machining of the end faces of each panel was done one end at a time for the Beylerbeyi Tower. For the Ortaköy Tower, the panel was set up between two facing machines and both ends were machined in the one set-up of the panel; a gauge was used to ensure, as nearly as possible, the correct absolute length for each panel. Measurements were taken on completion of machining, and if necessary, very minor corrections were calculated for succeeding panels.

112. As a result of the care taken, no panels had to be returned for re-machining after putting into the trial assembly, and the top surface over the four panels at each splice level of the legs was very plane, thus avoiding problems at the corners with interconnecting diaphragms, etc.

113. The attention to absolute accuracy of panel sizes and bolt hole dimensions produced a further major benefit when one of the Ortaköy portal web panels was completely wrecked through careless unloading in the port of Istanbul. Although it had been normally specified practice for the portals of these panels to be reamed while in trial assembly, together with corresponding portions of the legs, a replacement panel was made with holes drilled full size working entirely from the theoretical dimensions. This was found to fit perfectly to the rest of the portal and the legs during erection and by this means the replacement was provided in three weeks. Otherwise it would have been necessary to send the other adjacent panels back to the shop or to carry out time-consuming reaming or even drilling of holes during erection.

114. For the top of the legs under the saddles on the Beylerbeyi Tower, the top sections were assembled complete, including the top diaphragm and diaphragm stiffeners, and machined in one operation. The facing machines used for the Ortaköy Tower did not have adequate capacity for this but, by taking careful length measurements on the top of section 7 in the assembly and suitably adjusting the lengths for machining of the panels for section 8, the resulting top face when assembled against the saddle was found to be entirely satisfactory.

115. Particular characteristics of the two shops caused different arrangements to be used for the trial assembly of each tower. For the Beylerbeyi Tower (Fig. 22) the shop was long enough for the whole length of each leg to be laid down in a running assembly progressing down the shop. But because of limited crane height the legs had to be laid down with their smaller cross-sectional dimension vertical, i.e. with the inner panels of each leg on the floor. This meant that the trial assembly of the portals with their corresponding leg sections had to be carried out as a separate operation after the leg panels were released from the running leg assembly.

116. The shop in which the Ortaköy Tower (Fig. 23) was fabricated had sufficient height to allow assembly of the legs with the front (or rear) faces uppermost. This meant that the portals could be assembled against one leg during its assembly. On the other hand, this shop was not long enough to accommodate the complete tower height, so twice during the work sections of the legs had to be moved back along the shop for a new start. There appeared to be a marginal net advantage in time with this arrangement, particularly when

Fig. 22 Shop assembly of Beylerbeyi tower

Fig. 23 Shop assembly of Ortaköy tower

the requirements for checking the top leg sections against both the top portal and the saddles were allowed for.

Main cable wire manufacture

117. The wire was of the normal cold-drawn, hot-dip galvanized type. The steel was made and rolled into 10 mm dia. rods in the wire manufacturer's works. After patenting (special heat treatment and quenching) it was reduced in seven passes on a multiple, straight-line drawing machine to a black wire 4·92 mm in diameter. It was then annealed, pickled, galvanized and coiled in a continuous process. The diameters of the immersed draw-off spool in the galvanizing bath, and of the upper take-off sheaves, and the heights of the latter, were adjusted until the desired coiling characteristics were obtained.

118. The physical properties required by the contract specification were as given in Table 8. Wire which just met this specification would be entirely satisfactory for the bridge design once it wasin place in the cables. In order to ensure the most trouble-free cable spinning and the most predictable completed cable dimensions, the Contractor added the further requirements that the mean diameter of the whole order should be 5 mm ± 0·01 mm, and that elongation should meet a 6% target (not mandatory); after galvanizing, upper and lower limits were placed on the 'dead cast' diameter (diameter of an unrestrained single turn cut from a coil) and an upper limit on the 'lift' (height by which one end of the single free turn rose above the floor); specifications were laid down for means of forming and securing the coils and identifying the ends; and the nominal coil weight was agreed with the selected manufacturer at 350 kg (later increased to 400 kg for part of the order). Typical physical properties achieved were a tensile strength of 159–164 kg/mm², yield point of 129 kg/mm², elongation of 5·6 (minimum 4·8%) and galvanizing of 335 g/m². The average wire diameter for the whole order was 4·9999 mm.

119. The further specifications on secondary straightness characteristics and coiling procedures, and the co-operation of the manufacturer in adhering to or improving on these, are almost certainly the major reasons for the successful site reeling at speeds generally 50% and sometimes 90% higher than those used previously on suspension bridge construction. The lower nominal coil weight selected, averaging 356 kg rather than the 450 kg or 700 kg of other recent bridges with which the Author has been connected, is also believed to have contributed to this improvement. The increased number of stops for

Table 8. Contract specifications for wire

Diameter:	5 mm + 0·08 mm − 0·05 mm
Tensile strength:	157–180 kg/mm²
Yield Point (0·2% elongation)	120 kg/mm² minimum
Elongation (on 250 mm after break)	4% minimum
Galvanizing	275 g/m² minimum, plus dip tests. On 3 × diameter, without fracture of the steel or cracking of galvanizing such that it could be removed with the bare fingers.
Straightness	No deviation at 135 kg tension on 30 m suspended length

splicing seems to have been more than counterbalanced by easier loading and running of the smaller coils.

120. One unexpected problem arose in the transportation of the wire to site. It was known that on previous jobs where sea transport had been used for this easily damaged material there had been problems of corrosion and of damage due to inexpert slinging at the very many points of transfer. It was therefore initially decided to use overland trucking direct from the wire works to the bridge site; this had proved very successful for the Severn and New Quebec bridges. Inspection of the first loads delivered to site showed, however, a considerable amount of mechanical damage to the galvanizing and sometimes to the steel itself. It appeared that this was brought about by impacting between the turns of wire where they crossed each other, within or between coils, caused by vibration in transit. Various methods of packing and separation of the coils were tried but without success. It was concluded that truck transport over 2000 km of eastern European roads was very different from over 400 km of roads in England or Canada. Delivery was then changed to Rhine barge and shipping, with local trucking to the site. The coils were wrapped in paper and hessian, expert supervision was provided at all loading and transfer points, and ships with single sealed holds for the wire cargo alone were used. By these means the whole of the remaining wire was delivered with virtually no losses.

Deck fabrication

121. The various panels, which would later be site-assembled to form 17·9 m long sections of the box deck, were each fully shop fabricated complete with site weld preparations and part protective treatment. Production of the top deck panels was divided between Italy and the Contractor's UK works, the corner units were made in Italy, and the bottom, side and footway panels and the diaphragms were made in the UK works.

122. For the similar, but smaller, box deck for the Severn Bridge difficulties had arisen during the site assembly in achieving the correct cross-section of the box, particularly the roadway cross-falls, and therefore also in aligning the partly bolted connexions between the perimeter panels and the diaphragms; as a further consequence, tedious manual levelling of the roadway panel surface had to be carried out. This distortion of the cross-section was believed to be caused by somewhat unpredictable contraction of the partially restrained longitudinal assembly welds; this was generally less than expected, and was allied to 'growth' caused by imperfections in the straightness of adjacent panel edges. With nine seams across the top but only six across the bottom, the accumulation of these variations caused rotation of each half of the cross-section. With the 50% wider box at Bosporus these effects could have been expected to cause even greater difficulties. To overcome them, two measures were taken.

123. Tight tolerances were laid down for panel widths and edge straightness and these were rigorously enforced at the works. The tolerance adopted was $+0$ to -2 mm on the theoretical panel width in the completed box; i.e. it was assumed that any site weld contraction would be countered by 'growth', and it was also recognized that experience showed that normal shop practice generally resulted in oversized rather than undersized dimensions. The same

tolerance was applied to the length of all panels in order to reduce site difficulties caused by the ends of completed sections being out-of-plane.

124. For the bolted connexions between the transverse stiffeners on the perimeter panels and the diaphragms, the holes around the edges of the diaphragms were slotted horizontally, with the exception of those for the panels immediately to either side of the bridge centre line. The object of this was to allow for the remaining unpredictability of total width, while maintaining the more important vertical dimensions of the cross-section, including the roadway surface. The degree of success of these measures is discussed in §§ 188 and 189.

125. Some details of the fabrication of the top (roadway) panels deserve mention. For the triangular trough stiffeners, early investigations were made in Italy and the UK into production by longitudinal continuous forming from flat strip. It was, however, concluded that the required accuracy and consistency could most confidently and economically be achieved by pressing from prepared plates in half panel lengths; the half lengths were welded together before being attached to the deck plates. Very satisfactory troughs, as regards cross-section and straightness, were produced by these means.

126. The high standard of flatness required in the finished top panels was achieved by suitable precambering of the jig beds in both directions.

127. Welding of the obtuse continuous fillets between the troughs and the deck plates was carried out differently in the two works. In Italy means were developed of making satisfactory welds without excessive distortion of the panels in a single run in the horizontal position using submerged-arc boom machines. These had four heads, which completely welded both sides of two troughs at the same time (Fig. 24). In the UK works the panels were tilted and the welds made by hand in the gravity position.

128. The open-sided triangular corner units were very asymmetrical and therefore prone to distortion in welding. Efforts were concentrated on developing methods and sequences so as to reduce to a minimum any bowing, either vertically or horizontally, or twisting in the completed units. The target for straightness of all three free edges, on leaving the shops, was a maximum deviation of 6 mm. This was generally achieved and reduced considerably the problems of pulling-in and fairing these units to the rest of the section during site assembly. For the cantilever stubs, which were to connect with the footway panel transverse stiffeners, the spacing, depth and vertical edge alignment in two planes were checked in specially made gauge jigs and also by periodic trial against footway panels which were retained at the works for this purpose.

Viaduct fabrication

129. The methods used for the viaduct fabrication were generally what is normal for large box girders, modified as necessary to suit the very large size of these boxes. The cross-sectional dimensions of 3·00 m wide × 3·87 m deep make them possibly the largest to have been delivered from a fabricating shop in single pieces.

130. At the time of detailing and fabricating these box girder viaducts, the Merrison requirements were being progressively issued for such structures in the UK. As it was built outside the UK, the Bosporus Bridge was not subject by statute to these, but it was no surprise when instructions for some similar

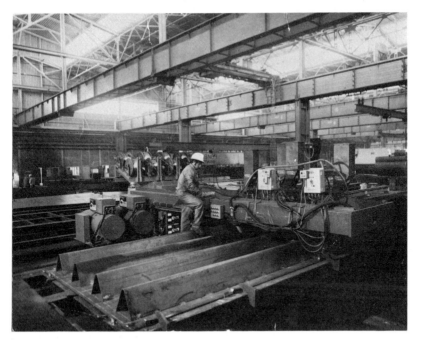

Fig. 24 Welding of deck panels in Italian works

variations to the design were received.   Intensive efforts had to be made in the drawing offices and shops to accommodate these changes with the minimum of disruption or delay to the fabrication.

131.   The girders were cambered positively and negatively along the length of the four or five continuous spans, to allow for the subsequent addition of the composite deck slab concrete as well as for self-weight.   This was effected by slight angular changes at each splice, the individual boxes between splices being straight.   To ensure the accuracy of these camber changes, and having regard to the great depth of the boxes, a running assembly of three successive boxes at a time was laid out in the shop, the splice bolt holes being finally reamed at this stage.

132.   In order to check the fit of the cross-girders and cantilever brackets, the two girders of most of the first span of each viaduct were assembled complete with these items (Fig. 25).   They are connected to the box girders solely by machined end-facing plates bearing directly against the webs of the boxes, and fastened by friction grip bolts.   There was no provision for any adjustment for length or inclination.

133.   Despite the very great care taken in the fabrication and machining of the cross-girders and cantilevers, and the adjustments made to the box girder fabrication methods as a result of the first shop assembly, it did not prove possible to achieve satisfactory standards.   Shimming at site was necessary for the cross-girders, as the laterally stiff box girders could not accommodate even 1 mm difference in length between successive cross-girders; tapered shimming

Fig. 25 Shop assembly of viaduct steelwork

was required to align the cantilevers so that their ends, with a 6·7 m cantilever relative to 970 mm deep connexions to the boxes, could be correctly fastened to the edge beams.   This added considerably to erection time and cost.   From experience on several bridges by different designers and fabricators, the Author considers that no practical fabrication procedures can give acceptable results with this end-face type of connexion.

134.   The tubular columns for the viaducts, 1·5 m in diameter, up to 48·6 m long (maximum length of shop fabrication 16·5 m), and of plate between 14 mm and 30 mm thick, were made from sections about 2·5 m long.   Each of these was rolled in the fabricating shop from plate and formed into tube sections with a partial penetration longitudinal butt weld.   For the circumferential welds joining together successive sections of each column, an arrangement of radial jacks was used to ensure exact alignment.

Shop protective treatment

135.   All exterior surfaces of the steelwork were required to be prepared by grit-blasting and flame zinc-spraying.   For the Beylerbeyi Tower, the viaducts and the deck steelwork made in Italy, hand grit blasting was used; this was followed by automatic zinc-spraying with multiple guns on a travelling portal which could spray simultaneously three sides of a unit.   For the deck panels fabricated in the UK automatic shot blasting equipment was used; in this case the zinc-spraying was by hand.   In all shops the subsequent priming and finishing paint coats were applied under cover.   For fabrication of the Ortaköy Tower in Sicily a particular problem was to seal the painting sheds adequately against dust blown in by sirocco winds from North Africa.

Erection

136. From an erection viewpoint, the Bosporus suspension bridge, although of larger dimensions, was of the same type as the Severn Bridge. Most of the technical erection problems presented to the Contractor were similar.[5] The changes from the methods adopted at Severn, and the reasons for these changes will be emphasized here, together with the means used to deal with the few design features which were different. In some instances, reference will also be made to experience on the Pierre Laporte Bridge at Quebec City, Canada, in the erection of which the Author's company had been engaged in the interval between the Severn and Bosporus bridges.

137. Some local factors affected all phases of the erection. Owing to the steep sides of the Bosporus 'valley' which has very narrow level areas adjacent to the water, and the density of buildings and trees which could not be disturbed, the working sites were limited to little more than the areas occupied by the piers and anchorages. Stockpiling of materials on site was virtually impossible and the steelwork for the towers and viaducts had to be delivered only a few days ahead of erection. An area was, however, available for about 80% of the main cable wire, although this required a haul of about 200 m on steep roads to the spinning machinery area. Space suitable for stockpiling the heavy steelwork, even at a distance from the site, was not readily available in the Istanbul area, but a useful area of quay in the port on the Asian side was obtained some time after the start of the contract.

138. Access for materials from the port to the sites by road was very limited. The roads to the anchorage and viaduct areas were very steep and narrow; on the Asian side access was further restricted by a palace gardens and historic buildings. The tower pier sites adjoined main streets, but there were axle-load and length restrictions between these and the ports. In any case, road haulage facilities of the low-loader or heavy long load trailer type were virtually non-existent in Istanbul. Further factors were the lack of adequate quayside cranes and the fact that suitable or available berths for a particular ship might not be on the same side of the Bosporus as that for which the bridge cargo was destined.

139. Almost all the permanent steelwork and most of the heavy equipment was therefore unloaded by floating cranes into barges and unloaded at site by derricks, of 35 ton capacity at each pier and 10 tons at the deck assembly site. For individual pieces weighing over 35 tons, floating cranes had also to be used at the pier sites. Obtaining the services of one of the three floating cranes or of the few suitable flat barges in competition with other port users was often a major factor in maintaining the inevitably tight delivery programme.

140. A third local condition which had to be constantly borne in mind in the planning of the erection methods was the lack of plant hire facilities. In Western Europe and North America it has become normal practice to rely on hired heavy mobile cranes for the initial erection of equipment and for the occasional very heavy or high lifts, and to get out of unplanned difficulties. For Bosporus, every conceivable lift had to be planned so as to use the cranes being put on the contract or the special equipment devised and provided. For general purpose duties two 25 ton truck mounted cranes were purchased; this was the largest size which was considered able to use the roads between and within the various sites.

141. Early enquiries indicated that electricity supplies sufficient for all requirements could not be obtained from the municipal system, and that in any case interruptions and major voltage variations would be a problem. It was therefore arranged that all major items of plant would be diesel powered and 1100 kVA of diesel generating capacity was provided to supply welding equipment, lighting, electric derricks and winches, and specialized equipment which had to be electrically driven.

Tower erection

142. The basic equipment for tower erection consisted of two special luffing jib tower cranes to each tower, operated by winches at ground level and climbed by rope tackle (Fig. 26). The advantages, compared to the previous British practice of a single special derrick on a hydraulically climbed structure which carries all the machinery, were:

(*a*) individual cranes close to each leg of the tower need have only very short radius capacity for heavy lifts; the portal components could be lifted by each crane taking one end; this resulted in much lighter cranes;

(*b*) the weight to be climbed was further and substantially reduced by leaving the operating machinery at ground level; the weight achieved for each crane was 90 t including kentledge for a maximum duty of 45 t, compared with a 180 t climbing weight for a 24 t duty with the Severn Bridge cranes;

(*c*) as a result of the lighter weight, the smaller operating radius and closer position to the tower leg, the horizontal loads applied to the legs were also much reduced; the maximum at one corner was under 10 t compared with 57 t at Severn; moreover, approximately equal loads were applied to opposite sides of the leg and the problems of distortion of the leg cross-section were thus avoided;

(*d*) the proximity of the cranes to the leg and the shorter operating radius eased the problems of handling panels into position in wind;

(*e*) two cranes were available for simultaneous operation on each tower;

(*f*) the rope tackle for climbing the cranes was much faster and more foolproof than an incremental jacking system, and the winches used for this could be used for several later erection phases;

(*g*) the main crane operating winches could be used for the later deck and viaduct erection systems.

143. The cranes had non-rotating lattice masts with a total height approximately equal to two standard 19·5 m lifts of the tower. The weight of the crane and the vertical operating loads were carried by a plated footstep bracket below the base of the mast; stabilization of the crane and transmission of horizontal operating and wind loads were provided by two upper framed brackets carrying rollers which bore against the corner rectangular hollow section (RHS) members of the mast. Both types of bracket were connected to the tower through identical transferable connexion plates, each with two-pin fastening to the top outer corners of each lift of the legs.

144. In service, the two roller brackets were close together at the top of the last completed lift of the tower leg, supporting the crane mast at about its mid-point. In preparation for climbing the crane, the upper of the two roller

Fig. 26 Tower erection cranes at lowest level

brackets was raised to the top of the newly erected lift; this did not put the crane out of commission. For each actual climb the raising tackle was reconnected to a cathead placed on the existing top of the leg and the footstep bracket was freed. When at the new height the brackets were fixed to the next level of the pinned connexion plates. As the outer faces of each tower leg were battered, and as it was desired to operate the cranes with their masts vertical and at a constant distance from the leg, the roller bracket frames incorporated means of adjusting the rollers relative to the face of the leg.

145. The rotating superstructures of the cranes were slewed by ropes diverting through sheaves in the superstructure and operating on a bull wheel fixed to the top of the mast.

146. The crane operating winches were of fairly conventional four drum type. Two drums of 7·5 t capacity were used for the two ends of the balanced (no becket) eight-part or six-part hoist tackle. A third 7·5 t drum served the derricking tackle and the fourth drum (for slewing) was of 3 t capacity. Each winch was powered by two 93 h.p. diesel engines with hydraulic torque convertors.

147. Once the towers were complete these cranes remained at the tower tops for service in erection of the cable, deck and viaduct. When the hoist drums of their main winches were in use for deck or viaduct lifting schemes, the alternative facility of a single line 5 t hoist was used for the lighter duties then required at the towers.

148. The problems of safely lifting panels of the type in these towers, to heights of up to 165 m in the winds which prevail in estuarial or channel locations in Europe, are formidable. For the Bosporus Bridge the typical panels (19·5 m × 5·6 m) had 60% greater area than those for the Severn. Clearly, increased precautions had to be taken if erection was to be possible in other than the very occasional dead calm conditions without undue risks. The features of the crane design which contributed to safer and easier handling at the erection level have been described in § 142.

149. In order to give the maximum practicable control during the lift which took up to 19 min, twin tensioned guide ropes were provided at each leg, between the piers and brackets forming part of the upper gangway system. The two bottom corners of each panel being lifted were connected by short wire rope pennants to shackles running on the guide ropes. This improvement over the single central guide rope to each tower as at the Severn and the changes in the top level handling allowed the much larger panels to be erected in winds up to about the same limit, about 25 km/h, as at the Severn. It appears unlikely that the wind speed limit for safe erection for this type of tower can be raised any further, and the resulting lost time must be accepted. During erection of the Bosporus towers, wind stopped the lifting of major pieces on about 30% of the days on which it had been intended to erect them. Overall weather loss was about 16% of the total tower erection period.

150. For the bolting-up of the vertical corner seams, air-operated two-man climbing cages were used. The seams, except those connecting to the portals, were internal; this meant that great care had to be taken to avoid accidents caused by the cages catching on the many protruberances. On all the internal work it had to be constantly borne in mind that the heights from which a man could fall were just as great as outside; the inevitably lower standard of lighting, and the greater contrasts of light, allied with the many obstructions and the sometimes deceptive sense of safety, added to the risks. This was a cause of particular concern later when a less skilled type of labour was being used for the internal painting. With the advent of lightweight and easily transferable mechanically operated staging, there is little doubt that work such as bolting-up is now safer outside structures such as these towers.

151. It was originally specified that the set-back of the tower saddles by about 1 m, necessary for balanced cable construction, should be achieved by fully bending the towers backward, as had been done at the Severn and on a few other bridges with relatively flexible towers. It was expected that the rope holdback system used for this would again serve in addition as the necessary damping device against aerodynamic oscillation. Checks carried out

early in the contract showed, however, that the effect of the full wind load on the pulled-back tower would be seriously to over-stress the screwed rods at the splices. The towers were already in fabrication so it was not possible, without serious delay, to strengthen the splices so as to solve the problem by this means alone. Neither was it practicable to redesign the tower top to provide for the other conventional solution, of maintaining the towers approximately vertical and making provision to jack up the saddles at almost full vertical dead load (about 9950 t in this case). A compromise was therefore devised.

152. Sufficient modifications were incorporated in the tower tops and saddles to allow the latter to be offset and jacked under vertical loads up to that from three completed main cable strands; this was only about 400 t. The number of screwed rods was increased to the extent reasonably practicable at some splices. This allowed the tower tops to be pulled back about 300 mm, which was considered to be the minimum which would ensure that the holdbacks acted effectively as a damping system.

153. The saddles were erected with a set-back of about 700 mm. The towers were pulled back the permitted distance of 300 mm, thus giving the saddles the required total set-back. The temporary footwalk system was erected and the first three strands of each cable were spun. The saddles were then jacked relative to the tower tops until they reached their central, final, positions; in reality the tower tops moved under the saddles, which were now more or less fixed in space by the action of the cable strands. At the same time the holdback strands were correspondingly pulled in. It had been calculated that three main cable strands provided enough deflexion stiffness so as to 'prop' the tower top effectively in future wind load conditions, thus relieving the load on the splices. Thereafter, the towers were treated, and behaved, as if they had been fully pulled back before start of cable construction.

154. During tower erection, the damping/holdback system was first attached when erection reached the centre portals. When the towers were complete and the footwalk strands and mesh were erected, giving some support, the holdbacks were raised to the upper portals. The system performed well in its damping function and the oscillations observed at any time were negligible.

155. As one of the final operations in the bridge construction, the climbing cranes had to be removed. After preliminary moves at the tower top they were lowered complete, by tackle from the saddles. The top of the crane was allowed to swing outward from the tower face, while rollers guided the bottom of the mast against the tower. With the mast base down to the pier, the crane was tied in to the tower while the superstructure was dismantled using the lowering tackle. The mast was then lowered off and dismantled. This method avoided the weather delays and possible risks which would have attended any scheme for piece-small dismantling of the cranes at the tower tops.

Cable construction

156. The temporary footwalk system for cable spinning, other cable activities and deck access, was of the same basic type which had been developed for the Forth Road Bridge. The progressive improvements which had been incorporated at Severn and Quebec were continued. Much of the material from the Quebec footwalk systems was used, as were several other items of equipment which had been used in the cable construction there.

157. One particular change which had been proved at Quebec was the reduction of the 25 mm footwalk floor strands from eight to six. The welded floor mesh had been found to perform adequately with supporting strands at only 150 mm (nominal) centres as against the 300 mm spacing which had been used previously. This reduced the number of pieces of supporting strand which had to be erected for the whole system to eight only; six floor strands and two handstrands, all continuous from anchorage to anchorage.

158. Even this small number did not have to be erected from the water. The number of closures of the very busy Bosporus international waterway was reduced to only two in the whole bridge construction. In the first one 26 mm track rope was laid across and lifted to the tower tops, approximately on the bridge centre line. During the second closure a 16 mm hauling line was erected on the same path. All the floor and hand strands for both footwalks were pulled across on the resulting bi-cable high-line system without any interruptions to shipping. All subsequent operations in completing the footwalk systems were planned so that no operations from the water were needed; e.g. the crosswalks were pulled out along the strands by tower-to-tower hauling lines.

159. Cable spinning followed the usual basic principles; the method used was of two bights from one end with powered unreelers. Several significant changes were, however, made to equipment and detail procedures, with the aims of higher output at reduced cost.

160. The tramway speed was increased from the 220 m/min used on most previous bridges such as Severn to 300 m/min. This appears to be about the maximum speed worth using on a bridge of this span; a slightly higher speed has been shown to be practicable on one bridge of considerably longer span and overall length.[6]

161. This increase in tramway speed required an approximately equal increase in output from the wire feed machinery, while maintaining the advantages of powered unreeling, i.e. faster acceleration, lower tramway power and much lower spinning wire tensions; these last result in greater reliability and safety of the wire handling equipment and procedures along the bridge.

162. Prior to Bosporus, the wire feed machinery for this system had consisted of reeling machines, a stock of detachable reels, and separate unreeling machines which could accommodate the same reels. The unreeling machines were powered by complex electro-hydraulic drives. The time taken to change reels on an unreeler can be a significant interruption to spinning, so the tendency was towards heavier and heavier reels; 7 tons, or 10–20 trips of typical cable lengths, was the minimum for powered unreelers, but up to 24 ton reels have been used with unpowered unreeling. The area required for the reeling operation was such that it generally had to be remote from the spinning anchorage; transport and lifting facilities for the full and empty reels, and a stock of between about 100 and 400 reels, were therefore required.

163. The basic innovation for Bosporus was a combined reeling and unreeling machine with twin non-removable reels (Fig. 27). This led to the following advantages:

> (a) as the 'reel change' operation was reduced to only that time needed to cut the wire and make one splice, it could be easily accommodated between successive trips for one machine; there was therefore no

Fig. 27 Reeling and unreeling equipment

longer any advantage in large reels and the capacity could be reduced to four trips (under 4 tons) for the longest likely bridge;

(b) the reels could be simply mounted on a fixed shaft, and permanently connected to the drive and brakes, thus obviating the complex mechanisms for rapid loading and unloading of reels and connexion and disconnexion of the drive and brakes;

(c) the reduced reel weight and the elimination of reel changing facilities (which had commonly required cantilever mounting of the reel) permitted a much lighter structure;

(d) the reduced reel weight produced a corresponding reduction in the power required (which is mainly for acceleration and deceleration); this was particularly valuable in view of the higher operating speeds.

(e) the lower power requirement made it possible to use commercially available large air motors; these are particularly suitable for this application because: (i) variable speed reversing motion is easily achieved by simple control valves with no auxiliary equipment; (ii) the equipment is of a type familiar to normal site maintenance staff; (iii) of the four unreeling machines required for two-bight spinning, at any one time two are idle except for brief adjustments and the other two, feeding the loaded wheel, are only at full power for brief acceleration periods; the average power demand is therefore much less than the required aggregate installed capacity and

47

Table 9. Outputs of Bosporus and three earlier bridges

	Forth	Severn	Quebec	Bosporus
Total cable length*	2127 m	1703 m	1130 m	1656 m
First 4000 t:				
Working Weeks:	20½†	19	11	12½‡
Nominal hours/week:	96	80	118	91
Total available spinning hours	1474	1236	986	941
Net spinning hours (excluding weather and equipment losses)	776	797	887	682
Maximum output (t/h) §				
Best single days output:	9·0	6·0	6·3	7·9
Last 4 weeks' output:	5·7	5·2	5·2	6·7

*Possible output reduces as the length decreases, particularly during initial 'learning' period.
† Excludes storm damage repairs.
‡ Excludes jacking of tower saddles.
§ Based on available spinning hours.

low capacity compressors can therefore be used, together with a suitable volume of air receivers; individual steam engines with a central boiler would probably be equally suitable, but are now less easily obtained.

(*f*) the space required was reduced to a single area, which was less than half that required previously; this could be adjacent to or on the anchorage and site preparation and foundation costs were correspondingly reduced;

(*g*) reel transport facilities and the costly stock of special reels were eliminated;

(*h*) the reduced amount and simpler character of the equipment considerably reduced the labour and time required for installation and proving, and there was a reduction in operating labour and supervision.

164. In operation, wire was being reeled on to one of the two reels to each machine, while at the same time the other reel was feeding one of the bights to one of the two spinning wheels serving the 'spinning' cable. The total width over the two narrow reels was within that which could be accommodated with a single uncoiling line or a single input sheave on the counterweight tower.

165. The development of this type of reeling/unreeling machine and process (for which patent applications have been filed in the UK and other countries), together with some simplification of other items, reduced the total capital expenditure in 1971 on the wire feed machinery to about 20% of that which had been spent in 1960 for the Forth Road Bridge; allowing for inflation, the reduction in cost was even greater. At the same time greatly increased consistent outputs were achieved. Table 9 shows comparisons of three earlier bridges and Bosporus, for spinning of the first 4000 tons and for maximum outputs.

166. The daily reeling output per machine had to match the optimum

spinning output at the new, higher tramway speeds.   This required significantly higher reeling speeds than had been used before.   These were comfortably
achieved, and indeed exceeded, and there was no need to work any longer
hours on reeling than on spinning.   The maximum speed which had been
used at Severn and Quebec was 360 m/min.   The normal speed at Bosporus
was about 560 m/min, and frequently speeds of up to 700 m/min were used.
In the early days of spinning there was some incidence of kinking in the wire
from the reeling process, not only at high speeds.   This was completely eliminated by minor adjustments to the swift design and operating methods.

167.   Another aspect of the equipment and methods which received serious
consideration during the planning stage was the signal system, particularly
in view of the problems of implementing the complicated process of cable
spinning with a language barrier.   Duplicated light signal systems for wire
adjustment were provided on each side of each walk so that there was one for
each wire; the individual wires and their associated equipment were identified
by colour throughout the bridge.   Available techniques made this possible
without increase in the quantities of signal cable and with small, economical
and easily installed panel units.

168.   The improvements more than fulfilled expectations; despite the language problems, efficiency in the first few days built up much more quickly than
on previous jobs and the ultimate operator efficiencies were at least equal to
previous standards.   The total time for cable spinning is given in Table 10.

169.   Regarding weather conditions, the wind on most days ranged between 10 and 40 km/h during the day.   Normal full speed spinning proceeded
in this, and was also possible in winds up to 50 km/h.   Reduced output could
be achieved in winds of up to 65 km/h.   The low weather loss in what was a
distinctly windy site for cable construction was largely due to the methods for
spinning in consistent winds which had been developed at Severn.

170.   Of the rather high equipment breakdown time noted in Table 10,
about half was due to two 'non-mechanical' factors.   About 40 h were lost
by complete stoppage of spinning to deal with the wire kinking in the early
stages of the job.   Almost 60 h of lost time were caused by slippage and failure
of the long splices of the tramway rope.   The extent of this was unprecedented
in the Author's experience.   No single cause or complete solution of the prob-

Table 10.

Spin 19 main strands to each cable (5305 t)	14 weeks 5 days
Interruption for saddle jacking	1 week
Spin additional backstay strands (131 t)	1 week 4 days
	17 weeks 3 days
For the 5305 t in the 19 continuous strands to each cable:	
Total available spinning time	1130 h
Effective weather loss	82 h (7·3%)
	1048 h
Equipment failures	216 h (20·6%)
Net spinning time	832 h

lem was found. The splices were made by a first-class operator with successful experience on previous cable spinning installations. Of the other possible factors, each method had been used before without trouble. These included a flexible rope construction (6 × 36, IWRC), splices only about 18 m long, operating speed of 300 m/min, high static tension (about 7 t, dictated by the main cable geometry) and deflexion sheaves at 90° to each other only 2 m apart (dictated by the anchorage configuration). These had not, however, all been used simultaneously on previous bridges; it is believed that their combination produced the failures. This may also indicate that the margin of safety on the splices for cable spinning tramways, which must necessarily violate many of the rules for permanent rope tramway installations, is much smaller than realized.

171. The arrangement proposed by the Contractor as part of his alternative tender for cable spinning, was that the required 10 414 wires in each main span cable should be divided into 19 strands of generally 548 wires. The alternative would have been 37 strands of about 282 wires, which would have given very short periods of continuous spinning, required more interruptions for changeovers and twice as many strand adjustments, and increased the costs of the anchorage steelwork, the saddles and the temporary cable formers. On the other hand, 548-wire strands were bigger than any spun before. However, the success of the methods used with the 438-wire strands at Severn, after the 304–328 wires at Forth, indicated that the larger strands should be practicable.

172. In the event, the advantages of the 19 strand arrangement were realized. Adjusting the strands through the tower saddles was, however, difficult, particularly for the bottom layer of the strands. The 60 t capacity of the planned equipment had to be doubled, and loads of up to about 75 t were required to move the strands. Lagging of bottom wires and 'birdcaging' were also a problem at times. It would seem that the strand size used here is close to the limit which is practicable with current methods of spinning in the saddles.

173. Three factors of the overall geometry of the bridge and its design presented particular problems in the cable spinning. The short unloaded side span or backstay cables had unusually steep slopes at their upper ends, the tangents being 0·589 at Ortaköy and 0·565 at Beylerbeyi, against main span tangents of 0·308. With balanced horizontal forces at the tower top, this caused the tension on the side span side of the saddles to be appreciably higher than that on the main span side. The measures used to deal with this in the permanent design, by additional strands in the side spans only, had the indirect effect of increasing further the unbalance in tension during the spinning of the main strands. As a result, friction coefficients in the tower saddles of 12·4% at Ortaköy and 11·5% at Beylerbeyi were necessary if adjusted wires were to stay in place. Most previous bridges had only required about 6%, and 10% had been the conventional limit (though generally not needed).

174. In practice, there was some slippage of adjusted wires into the side span, particularly at Ortaköy. The movement was between 10 and 30 mm. Being small and fairly uniform this did not seriously affect uniformity of wire sags in the side spans, but the strands took up spinning positions lower than those preferred. Complete strands did not move after their adjustment. It is clear that effective frictions are much greater for completed strands than for single wires, particularly in saddles with permanent separators between the vertical rows of strands, as adopted here.

Fig. 28 Spinning equipment at splay saddle

175. The anchorage design was such that the strands splayed equally up and down from the splay point and, in the complete bridge, the cable casting at this point was floating. In most large suspension bridges with parallel wire cables, the axis of the anchorage has been such that all the strands are deflected downwards by varying amounts, over a saddle at the splay point. The floating splay caused obvious problems in spinning and adjusting the upper strands. The possible solutions were limited by the type of strand anchorage, as compared with the fully rotating strand shoes on long 'eye-bar' links which had been used with the one or two previous examples of floating splays. The method adopted (Fig. 28) was:

(a) all upper strands were spun slightly above the top of the trough of the splay point casting; there were temporary upward extensions of the casting sides to take the horizontal splay; the vertical deflexion upward to the strand shoe was provided by placing the wires, as spun, under temporary inverted 'hook' type strand saddles just behind the splay casting;

(b) before adjustment of the completed strand, it was jacked down into its final position in the splay casting by means of a strap adjacent to the spinning saddles; these straps were maintained in position until all the upper strands were completed;

(c) when all the strands had been spun and adjusted, the cap was put onto the splay casting trough and bolted down; the temporary strand holding-down straps were then released and the casting was allowed to float free of its supports as dead load was applied to the cable.

51

176. The third particular cable spinning problem set by the design was the construction of the four additional backstay strands. After study by the Contractor of various alternative arrangements for the tower top anchorages, the most practicable scheme involved two horizontal strand shoes mounted on top of the tower saddle at its side span end (Fig. 29). The uppermost shoe was of larger diameter than the lower. For the inner pair of additional strands, the wires ran from one vertical strand shoe at the anchorage, up one side of the cable, round the lower saddle shoe, and down the other side of the cable to another vertical strand shoe. A similar arrangement from two further shoes at the anchorage to the upper shoe at the saddle formed the outer pair of additional strands.

177. These strands were constructed in pairs by the spinning wheels travelling between one anchorage and the adjacent tower. Unorthodox wire handling methods were developed to deal with the different direction of wire feed in each side span and the transition from vertical to horizontal shoes.

178. Compacting of the cables followed normal practice, two hydraulically operated machines with electric pumps being used. The average void ratios achieved were 20·7% at the compactor shoes while under pressure and 22·2% in straps, at 1 m centres. These values are respectively 0·7% and 0·4% better than the corresponding figures at Severn. This goes against the Author's previous opinion, apparently proved by comparison of the Forth and Severn results, that the compaction should be less efficient as strand sizes become larger. Moreover, the Bosporus results were achieved with the compactor rams generally operated at 40–50 t, on account of pump problems, rather than at their 60 t capacity.

179. The wrapping of the cables was carried out by four machines which had been designed and built for Quebec, with appropriate modifications for the cable diameter (including the different main and side span diameters) and electrical supply. The very heavy and complex wrapping machines used at Forth and Severn, with self-loading concentric reels of large capacity, rapid pusher-to-puller conversion, and hydraulically operated main drive and auxiliaries, had never realized in full the theoretical advantages of that type. For the Quebec bridge the emphasis was put on lightness. The machines were of the much simpler planetary type, carrying two reels, each limited to a weight which could be manhandled; the time for two or three changes per panel was considered to be outweighed by the other advantages of the light weight of the reels and machine. Several of the desirable features of the concentric wrapper were, however, incorporated in these new planetary machines. In particular, fingers were provided to pack the turns of wire tightly against the preceding turns as they were laid, and the reel brakes and wire fairleads were designed to provide high, consistent and predictable wrapping tensions.

180. On both Bosporus and Quebec bridges these machines gave high output with wrapping of very good quality. No gaps, however thin, were permitted between the turns of wire. At Bosporus, generous quantities of red lead paste were used to ensure that all the spaces between the main cable and wrapping wires were completely filled. One disadvantage of this, however, was that the consequent excess paste on the outside of the wrapping had to be cleaned off as it was not compatible with the specified paint system. This was a very tedious operation and it would have been preferable if the paste and the first paint coat had been compatible.

Fig. 29 Anchorage for additional backstray strands on tower saddles

181. Another factor which facilitated good wrapping derived from the compacting procedure and the dimensioning of the cable bands. It has been common practice to aim for a true circular cross-section inside the tightened cable bands; this requires that the cable be compacted to a slightly elliptical shape, and this remains between cable bands for the wrapping operation. At Bosporus the practice which had been developed for Severn was repeated; the cable bands were dimensioned so as to be offered up on a circular cable and, on tightening, to take up a final elliptical cross-section. This is of no consequence there, and it allows the cable to be compacted generally to a true circle, which greatly facilitates operation of the wrapping machine fingers.

Deck erection
182. A major decision which was taken at the tender stage was that the assembled box deck sections would not be themselves floated in the water as at Severn, but would be placed on a barge for lifting, with any necessary storage being on land. There were several reasons for this.
183. Serious painting problems had been caused by immersion at Severn, with long lasting consequences. The problem would have been magnified at Bosporus by the need to store a much larger number of sections for a longer period to meet the programme. A more expensive paint treatment would have been needed, and considerable deterioration, requiring extensive remedial treatment, was probable.
184. The experiments carried out for Severn had also shown that the sections could not be safely towed or pushed with the asymmetrical diaphragm

53

arrangement as required for the design. It would again have been necessary for an additional diaphragm to be provided and installed close to the end from which the first permanent diaphragm was inset 3·5 m. The weight of the additional diaphragms, if left in as at Severn, might have required additional material in the cables, towers or anchorages. The tenderer would have had to add the cost of this to his price, and installing the additional diaphragm would have added to the assembly time.

185. If the sections had been immersed, lifting would have had to be halted just above water level, to wash down with fresh water. Its avoidance gave programme and navigation advantages. Finally any risks of damage to the sections while in storage or being moved for lifting were virtually eliminated. This was of particular importance on the Bosporus where each year there are several instances of ships running into the shore, particularly in fog.

186. For assembly of the sixty 17·9 m long sections of the complete box sections from the imported fabricated panels, a yard was set up on one of the few level areas along the Bosporus, about 5 km north of the bridge site on the Asian side.

187. The desired overall programme required at least one deck section to be lifted on each good weather day, up to the stage when transverse joint welding became the limitation. The minimum assembly cycle possible for a pair of sections on each of the two stallage lines was estimated to be ten days, and therefore a stock of at least 24 completed sections was necessary by the start of lifting. To provide storage for these, as well as for the working stallages, derricks, and panel unloading, stockyard and transport facilities, required a minimum site area of 3·2 ha. An area of 5·6 ha was available; this allowed, at additional cost, the storage of 42 completed sections (Fig. 30). The requirement for large sites is one constructional disadvantage of the welded box deck type of suspension bridge; the comparative area required at Quebec for preassembly of bolted truss deck sections to meet the same lifting programme was only 1·3 ha; matched assembly was of course not necessary for these.

188. The measures to ensure the correct cross-section of the assembled sections described in §§ 123–4 were generally successful. The cross-fall over each half of the roadway was easily maintained. The specified flatness within each carriageway, transversely and longitudinally, was not however achieved, as had been intended, merely by putting bolts or pins in the peripheral holes between the diaphragms and the transoms on the outer panels. A considerable amount of manual levelling with subsequent reaming or redrilling of the bolt holes was found necessary. Although procedures were developed for this which minimized any delay to the assembly cycle, the additional work was undesirable.

189. It is felt that even greater attention to diaphragm dimensions and positioning of the holes should make it possible to be confident that bolting alone will produce acceptable shape and flatness, including allowance for subsequent welding movements. If the box deck is to achieve economies in construction costs comparable to those it offers in the materials used, it must be made possible to accept shop-derived dimensions with the same confidence as for modern truss fabrication processes. If this could lead to the elimination of matched assembly of all the sections, considerable further economies would result.

Fig. 30 Deck assembly area

190. Assembly of the deck sections required about 25 km of longitudinal butt welds to be made on site between plates 12 mm or 9 mm thick, the former being of high yield steel. None of the machine welding methods which had been used on previous similar jobs was considered entirely satisfactory. In particular, conventional backing strips, rectangular and typically 38 mm × 8 mm, if shop-applied to one plate edge had made it very difficult to achieve satisfactory welding quality even with multiple run procedures.[2] Site application of these had been very time-consuming and they were intolerant of minor irregularities in plate edge flatness. Protective treatment of the sharp corners and residual gaps between the strip and the plate had also given problems. Procedures which required initial gaps between the plates were also considered unsatisfactory, as these would have tended to produce inaccuracy in overall dimensions and excessive welding shrinkage.

191. Pending a solution to those problems, serious consideration was given to doing all the welding by hand, with some part of the procedures overhead. The required outputs could have been achieved but manpower would have had to be increased.

192. Considerable experimentation led to a completely new system for machine welding, which overcame all the previous problems. This is illustrated in Fig. 31 and is the subject of patent applications filed in the UK and other countries. The key feature was a small mild steel backing strip segmental in cross-section and only 18 mm wide with a 5 mm central thickness; burning through of such a thin strip was prevented by resting it in the close-fitting groove of temporary steel support blocks which acted as a heat sink. The blocks, with the backing strip, were held up against the underside of the joint

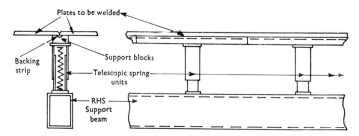

Fig. 31 Butt welding system

by telescopic spring units at close intervals. These were in turn supported by light RHS beams generally spanning between the stallage frames or diaphragms. Thus virtually no temporary welding was required on the underside of the plates.

193. The backing system could be set up very quickly just before welding. Complete cleanliness of the joint was therefore easily maintained. This permitted welds of excellent quality to be made consistently with a single run of the submerged arc process. The method was equally suitable for the weld along the lower sides of the box, at a 19° transverse slope.

194. The support blocks generally did not adhere to the backing strip and could be readily removed immediately the welding machine had passed beyond a particular part of the seam. They were suitable for reuse many times. The backing strip material was very cheap and its shape and small size eliminated the protective treatment problems. It is also very neat and inconspicuous in the completed bridge.

195. The ESAB 6AT submerged arc machines used proved to be very reliable and the whole operation dispelled the previously common prejudices against this process, as opposed to open arc with coated wire, for large-scale site welding.

196. The assembled sections were stored at all times on bogies. This greatly facilitated the many 'draughtboard' moves necessary when so many sections were simultaneously going into and out of a congested storage area. The risk of damage to these relatively fragile units from errors in jacking procedure required for transfers to or from fixed supports and bogies was also greatly reduced.

197. The barge for taking the sections from the loading-out jetty to the lifting position at the bridge was specially constructed at a local shipyard (Fig. 32). It was powered by four large steerable outboard motors and was operated on the system developed for the Severn and used again successfully on the St Lawrence for Quebec. The advantages of positioning and clearing very rapidly without semi-permanent moorings in currents which are strong and variable in direction were particularly valuable on the Bosporus with its intensive shipping traffic. No closures whatever were required for deck erection.

198. The characteristics of the Bosporus water required some modifications to the technique. The constant current of up to five knots with no slack water, and the depth of up to 60 m, required increased power and anchor

56

Fig. 32 Deck section carrier barge

capacity. The absence of tide meant that the section had to be picked up from the jetties by pumping out ballast water. Nevertheless, despite the barge having to stay in position as navigation guard until the lift was complete and then sail against the strong current back to the berth, cycles of less than 5 h between successive lifts were frequently achieved.

199. The arrangement for lifting the box sections was changed from the two-point support used at Severn to four-point lifting as normally used for truss sections. The advantages of this were:

(a) the unit load to be developed at the lifting connexions on the section was almost halved; these connexions were reduced to small cleats bolted to the internal diaphragms, with 22 mm dia. screwed rods passing through the upper plates to the block connexion; no additional stiffening or other permanent material was required and the few small holes could be easily sealed;

(b) stability during the lift was ensured with no more than the addition of light anti-yaw lines from air winches on the deck;

(c) the ability to control the levels of each end of the section separately greatly facilitated manoevring into position at the top, particularly in wind;

(d) elimination of the inclined stabilizing ropes below the lower block required by the two-point system, meant that the lower blocks could be at deck level; this eliminated the transfer procedure, involving temporary suspenders, which had been necessary about 8 m before completion of the lift for the sections in the middle quarter of the Severn main span, and as a result it was possible to lift two sections on most suitable days, even in the midspan area; it is calculated that this change saved at least one week on a critical part of the bridge programme.

200.   Temporary flanged connexions which had been added to the sections were bolted together immediately following erection, in order to maintain the alignment of the sections, to transmit axial and shear loads as the cable geometry changed, and to provide control against gust and aerodynamic wind effects.

201.   Welding of the transverse joints followed later, using machine and hand processes as found suitable.   This work was, as is usual on a suspension bridge, considerably controlled and affected by the intersection loads and changes of attitude.   As no permanent maintenance gantries were included in the contract, all the underside welding and final site painting were carried out from four temporary gantries which utilized the crosswalks from the cable footwalks and were supported from bogies running on the deck cantilevers.

202.   Remedial painting of the interior of the deck proved, as at Severn, to be a major operation.   These surfaces of the panels, except for narrow strips adjacent to the site welds, had received, as specified, the full treatment (two coats of red lead primer only) before despatch from the fabricating works. After shipping, storage at site, and abrasion by feet and equipment in the many months of assembly, erection, welding and installation of services, very little of this sensitive paint was left in an acceptable condition.   Inside the completed deck, the work of inspection, cleaning, debris removal and repainting was greatly hindered by problems of access, lighting and ventilation.   Unless the access points were severely limited the exposure to rain or humidity could cause further breakdown of repainted surfaces.   Altogether, the interior remedial work occupied a labour force of about 60 men for nine months, mostly after the bridge was open to traffic.

Viaduct erection

203.   The two box girder approach viaducts, under the cable side spans, were major bridges in themselves, requiring different techniques from the construction of the suspension bridge, but closely integrated with it.

204.   Selection of an erection scheme, and its relative timing in the bridge programme, was affected by the following factors:

(a) for the reasons given in §§ 137–9 the boxes, generally 15 m × 3·9 m × 3·0 m and weighing up to 41·7 t could be delivered only by barge to the tower pier sites;

(b) the nature of, and restricted access to, the ground under the viaducts ruled out movement of the boxes at ground level or operation there of mobile cranes of suitable capacity;

(c) the great height (about 48 m) above ground level of the spans nearest the towers and of the first rocker-ended tubular columns made it impracticable to provide adequate stability or safety against wind loading if erection were to be started from the tower ends of each viaduct.

205.   After consideration of several alternatives, the method chosen was to make the fullest use of the side span main cables.   The box girders, the columns in temporarily braced pairs and 'packages' of the cross-girders and cantilever brackets were all picked up at the side span face of the towers by tackle from a carriage on the cables.   This carriage was then run down the cables to the desired erection position and the components were lowered into

Fig. 33 Viaduct box girder erection.

position.   The winches which had served the tower cranes were used for these operations (Fig. 33).

206.   Erection was started at the anchorage (fixed) end of each viaduct. As the cables came below the girder level in the first spans, trestling had to be erected in front of the anchorages out to where the cable carriage had enough headroom to land the boxes.   The first few boxes were then rolled back into position using skates.

207.   A further major advantage of this scheme was that it avoided the additional weight of cranes or an erection device at the end of the cantilevered girder in each span.   This kept the stresses below those of the permanent condition and therefore no additional material was required in the boxes.   It also obviated the extensive engineering work which any erection overloading and consequent redesign would have required, particularly following issue of the Merrison report in the UK.

BROWN, PARSONS AND KNOX

208. Raising the ends of each span cantilever to align the boxes at the next column was also achieved by use of the erection tackle from the main cable, in association with temporary hinges at the joint just before the column.

209. This erection method imposed what are believed to be the heaviest rolling loads yet applied to completed large parallel-wire cables. The maximum reaction of 40 t at either end of the travelling carriage was distributed over four polyurethane tyred rollers, shaped to fit the cable. These performed satisfactorily themselves and no damage was caused to the main cable wires. There was, however, some distortion of the compacted cable cross-section and considerable breakage of the temporary straps; the latter was caused mainly by the edges of the rollers digging into the relatively 'soft' cable. It is felt that these effects could have been reduced by variations in the roller design, but the remedial work necessary (recompaction of the side span cables) was straightforward and non-critical to the programme. It was of minor significance compared to the advantages of the method.

210. On account of the methods used, and the reasons for them, viaduct erection had to follow cable spinning. This fitted well into the overall programming and resource allocation for the contract. It avoided adding to the supervision and labour peak of cable spinning plus deck assembly. Erection of the 3000 tons of steelwork in the two viaducts took only three months; despite a late start due to some equipment problems, it was completed only a few weeks after the lifting of the last main span sections.

211. As each viaduct was a continuous structure and composite with the concrete deck slab, there had to be a carefully calculated sequence for pouring of the latter. It was, however, permissible to start this before the completion of all steel erection; the method of transporting the steelwork, via the cables, eliminated obstruction of the erected spans and facilitated an early start to concreting. Access over the viaduct deck slab was possible by the time that the main span joint welding was sufficiently advanced for the mastic asphalt surfacing to be started in the main span.

212. One incident during viaduct erection could well have caused a major setback to the bridge programme. As mentioned previously, the steelwork was unloaded and stored in the port until immediately before it was required for erection. The quay used was considered to be completely sheltered, but on 26 February, 1973, a storm in the Marmara Sea sent unprecedented waves into the Bosporus. One or more of these penetrated to the quay and overtopped it to such an extent that six of the viaduct box girders, each weighing up to 40 tons, were swept off into 10 m of water. They were located by divers and raised by floating cranes. Damage by indentation and tearing was considerable, but it was found possible to repair them in situ, thanks to the resources of a local shipyard; they were ready within three weeks, just in time for erection. Had they been damaged beyond local repair, replacement would have taken several months.

Labour, supervision and safety
213. The labour employed on the site construction was entirely Turkish. Although no work of this nature had been carried out previously in the country there were no major problems in finding or training the necessary skills. In particular the efficiencies achieved in the complicated process of cable spinning were at least equal to previous standards in other countries and the output

60

and quality of the welders was extremely satisfactory. The total number employed on the superstructure reached a maximum of 448 during the closing weeks of the contract.

214. In accordance with Turkish law and practice, a 'bargaining contract' was agreed, before work started, with one of the major construction unions. All labour, of whatever craft, thereafter belonged to this one union. The contract, as well as laying down wage rates for various categories with increases over the two-year period, contained comprehensive details of fringe benefits and working conditions. No measured incentive bonuses were paid. The terms of the contract were fully observed and throughout the superstructure construction there were no stoppages of work caused by disputes.

215. The Author and all the Contractor's staff involved would like to pay tribute to the major part played by the Turkish workmen in the achievement of the bridge construction.

216. For most of the superstructure period British staff on site numbered 20. This included engineers, foremen and administratives. In addition there were up to 35 Turkish staff, of whom most were administrative, necessary for Turkish labour and commercial procedures. Names of the full-time operating staff are given in Appendix 1.

217. High safety standards were maintained throughout, particularly as a result of this aspect being constantly considered in the planning of erection methods and equipment. Serious-injury accidents were gratifyingly few. There was one fatality. This is greatly to be regretted; it should, however, be noted that it occurred as a result of an accident with a portable grinding machine and was not specifically related to the building of a major bridge.

Acknowledgements

218. The major work of constructing the substructure of the bridge has not been covered in this Paper, but the Author wishes to acknowledge the great help given to his company by their partners, Hochtief AG, who were responsible for that part of the contract. Their Site Manager was Dipl. Ing. O. Kotthaus, who also acted as Site Manager for the consortium.

219. The operational staff of Cleveland Bridge who were most involved in the superstructure construction are given in Appendix 1.

References

1. ROBERTS SIR GILBERT. Design of the Forth Road Bridge. *Proc. Instn Civ. Engrs*, 1965, **32** Nov., 333–405.
2. ROBERTS SIR GILBERT. Design and contract arrangements for the Severn Bridge. *Proc. Instn Civ. Engrs*, 1968, **41**, Sept. 1–48.
3. GOVERNMENT OF JAPAN. *Specifications for earthquake-resistant design of the Bosporus Bridge.* Government of Japan, November, 1967.
4. BIRDSALL B. Main cables of Newport Suspension Bridge. *Proc. Am. Soc. Civ. Engrs., J. Struct. Div.*, 1971, **97**, ST12, Dec., 2825–2835.
5. HYATT K. E. Severn Bridge: fabrication and erection. *Proc. Instn. Civ. Engrs.*, 1968, **41**, Sept., 69–104.
6. KINNY J. W. *et. al.* Verrazano-Narrows Bridge: fabrication and construction of superstructure. *Proc. Am. Soc. Civ. Engrs., J. Constn. Div.*, 1966, **92**, CO2, Mar., 168.

BROWN, PARSONS AND KNOX

Appendix 1. Consultant's and Contractor's Staff

Freeman Fox & Partners

Design and contract supervision:

Dr W. C. Brown
M. F. Parsons
C. R. Blackwell
D. R. Culverwell
M. Howley
N. G. Rees
C. W. Brown
D. W. A. Bower
H. B. Bailey
G. V. Andrews
W. Winterhalder
D. N. Holt
J. M. Kaluza
W. R. Halford

Site supervision:

Dr W. C. Brown (Partner in charge)
K. E. Hyatt
T. J. R. Gurney
H. G. Binnie
G. A. Pirie
H. K. H. Claxton
A. L. Burton
R. V. Long
S. P. Watkins
A. Chappell

Cleveland Bridge and Engineering Co. Ltd.

Project Director: H. S. G. Knox
Site Manager: F. N. Dinsdale
Chief Planning Engineer (Head Office):   H. Wilson
Chief Site Engineer: B. G. Blakeley
General Foreman: E. Winsper

Engineers (Head Office and Site):

S. E. A. Bensley
N. F. Hobson
J. I. McGibbon
C. E. Slater
B. Towlard

Engineers (Head Office):

M. Braithwaite
F. Dorn
J. Moran
R. Webb
Dr M. I. Webbe
B. Whittle
A. Whitworth

Engineers (Site):

M. Arkun
A. P. Deane
H. R. Hantal
S. Musluoğlu,
T. Onuk
T. Özmen

62

Foremen:
M. W. Belcher
B. P. Brooke
G. C. Charlton
R. A. Ince
J. R. Gough
J. Hartley
A. Joyce
N. F. Price
D. Shinner

Appendix 2. Contracting organization

Main Contractor:
The Anglo-German Bosporus Bridge Consortium comprising Hochtief, AG, Essen, West Germany (responsible for substructure and viaduct concrete deck) and Cleveland Bridge and Engineering Co. Ltd, (responsible for supply and erection of superstructure)
Principal Suppliers and Sub-contractors to Cleveland Bridge:
Costruzioni Metalliche Finsider, SpA, Livorno, Italy (fabrication of Beylerbeyi Tower, part of suspended deck and approach viaducts)
Antonio Badoni, SpA, Lecco, Italy (fabrication of Ortaköy Tower)
Arbed-Felten and Guilleaume, AG, Köln, West Germany (main cable wire. wrapping wire, erection ropes)
Limmer and Trinidad (International) Asphalt Co. Ltd, Dorking, England (surfacing of bridge carriageways and footways)
F. H. Lloyd Ltd, Wednesbury, England (cable band castings and splay saddle castings)
Peiner AG, Peine, West Germany (special friction grip bolts and high tensile screwed rods)
Brunton's (Musselburgh) Ltd, Musselburgh, Scotland (suspenders, crash barrier strands, footwalk strands and ropes)
Norman Cooper Construction Ltd, Newcastle-upon-Tyne, England (parapets)
Cunliffe Engineering Ltd, Thornaby, England (crash barrier posts and anchors)
Blackett, Hutton & Co. Ltd, Guisborough, England (strand shoe castings and suspender socket castings)
McCall & Co. (now BSC Reinforcement Group), Rotherham, England (anchorage pre-stressing bars)
British Paints Ltd (now Berger Chemicals), Newcastle-upon-Tyne, England; Colorificio Italiano Max Meyer, Milano, Italy, & Colorificio Attivo, SpA, Genova, Italy (paints)
KEP Ticaret ve Sanayi, Istanbul, Turkey (site painting)
Caswell Cranes and Erection Ltd, Winchester, England (climbing tower cranes)
Nominated Sub-Contractors for superstructure:
Demag AG, Düsseldorf, West Germany (roadway expansion joints at towers)
Ascinter Otis, SA, Paris, France (public and staff passenger lift machinery)
Rona Makina Sanayi ve Ticaret, AŞ, Istanbul, Turkey (lift steelwork)
Alarko Sanayi ve Ticaret, AŞ, Istanbul, Turkey (lighting and general electrical works)

Proc. Instn Civ. Engrs, Part 1, 1976, **60**, Aug., 503–530

7855   DISCUSSION

BOSPORUS BRIDGE

Part I: History of design

W. C. BROWN & M. F. PARSONS

Part II: Construction of superstructure

H. S. G. KNOX

Dr Brown

Brief reference is made in the Paper to the financing of the project but I would now like to explain its effect on the engineering of the work. The Government of the Republic of Turkey, in common with other developing countries, is short of foreign currency and is therefore obliged to spend what it has wisely, and to initiate foreign long-term loans whenever possible. As an associate member of the European Economic Community, she was in a position to approach the European Investment Bank (EIB) for such assistance. Nevertheless additional financial support was required and this was completed by direct bilateral loans from other countries. All loans were repayable over a period of 25 years, but the EIB finance could be expended only equally with the bilateral loans of the other participating EEC countries. Another feature of the financial agreement was that additional amounts (up to one-third of the above) were also available to the Turkish authorities for other purposes. This could be spent either in the country of origin or converted into Turkish lira. It was available only after signature of construction contracts; half available on the contract signing, the rest held back in case of overruns. Thus, although the main bridge contract was signed in 1970, additional finance was to be held over until July 1971 when the last approach viaduct contract was let.

221. About this time the UK Department of the Environment (DoE) issued new and untried interim rules for the design of box girder bridges, and of course this could affect this project. Those members of the Board of Consultants and others experienced in such construction were baffled, not only by the complexity of these rules but also by their unreality and conservatism. They wished to discard their relevance to this project. However, the technical advisers to the EIB were in no such independent position, nor were they so experienced. All monies due from the additional loan were frozen until the matter was resolved. This meant that finance for equipment urgently needed by the Turkish authorities was in jeopardy, and although, fortunately, no changes were made to the original design, nor was any work delayed on the approach spans, progress with the roadworks undoubtedly suffered badly and much of it remained to be completed after the bridge was opened.

222. The decision largely to ignore the rules was based on the following engineering

65

DISCUSSION

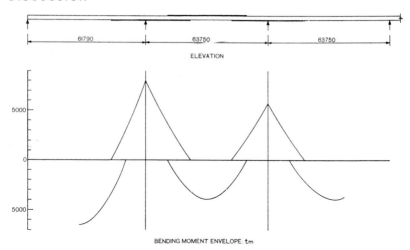

Fig. 34.

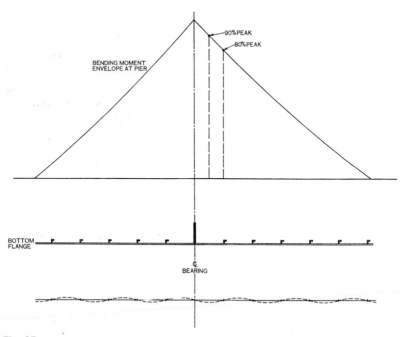

Fig. 35.

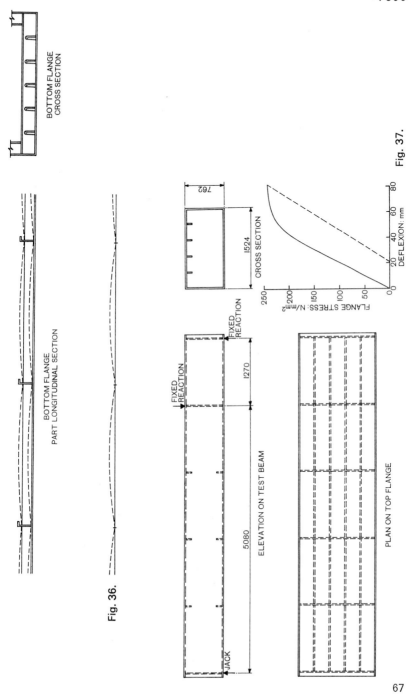

BOTTOM FLANGE
CROSS SECTION

BOTTOM FLANGE
PART LONGITUDINAL SECTION

Fig. 36.

762

1524

CROSS SECTION

FIXED
REACTION

FIXED
REACTION

1270

5080

ELEVATION ON TEST BEAM

JACK

FLANGE STRESS: N/mm²

250

200

150

100

50

0

0   20   40   60   80

DEFLEXION: mm

Fig. 37.

PLAN ON TOP FLANGE

DISCUSSION

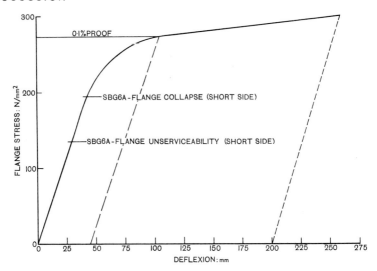

Fig. 38.

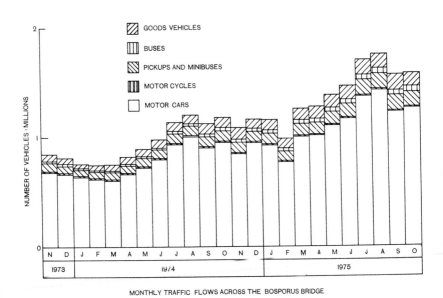

MONTHLY TRAFFIC FLOWS ACROSS THE BOSPORUS BRIDGE

Fig. 39. Monthly traffic flows across the Bosporus Bridge

68

philosophy reinforced by experimental work of Freeman Fox and Partners and the wealth of similar experience of Prof. K. Kloppel. Fig. 34, which is typical of all such spans, shows the extent and intensity of the compressive stress in the box girder flanges. All experienced designers must surely agree that the possibility of any plate or panel instability with the upper flange bonded to the concrete deck slab is so remote that it needs no further consideration. Thus the question of instability is restricted to the bottom flange, and in practice near the piers. It will be observed from Fig. 35 that the stress peaks near the pier and falls off rapidly over adjacent panels. In designs incorporating stiffened panels of such dimensions that the onset of yield, rather than theoretical Euler instability, is the determining factor (i.e. $l/r \not> 60$), the use of stiffeners placed on one of the plates provides considerable end fixity with respect to adjacent panels, as any longitudinal buckling in simple sinusoidal form between transverse stiffeners reduces the stiffener compressive deformation stress in alternate panels (Fig. 35). Weld distortion effects, which in addition usually deform the stiffeners in a most favourable manner, also serve to improve stability (Fig. 36). Whilst it is possible to argue from a theoretical base that these effects may be absent, and should be ignored 'to be on the safe side', such an approach will obviously lead to increasingly conservative results. To check these and other effects (such as combination of shear and axial stress) experiments were carried out on nominally mild steel specimens as shown in Fig. 37. The general results are shown in Fig. 38 and compared with the DoE Merrison Rules. The property of steel to adjust to local stresses also adds to the improvement between theoretical and actual behaviour. In my opinion, if recent experimental work is examined objectively, there can be little doubt that the rigid application of the DoE rules to conventional steel box girders of the type described in Part I is inappropriate.

223. Since opening day traffic using the bridge has been about 50% above prediction and the revenue such that the capital cost is almost recovered already. The current daily traffic of over 50 000 could well be up to 60 000 in 1976 (Fig. 39).

224. Although similar in general form to the Severn, this bridge is different in most other respects. Sir Gilbert Roberts, who retired before the tenders for this bridge were let, nevertheless was most helpful in giving advice and our thanks are due to him.

Mr Knox

With experience of four suspension bridges behind us when we approached Bosporus, my firm's main concern in dealing with the tight programme and competitive price was to try to set new standards throughout of economy in resources used. Every phase of the construction was looked at on the basis of whether work items done previously were necessary. For those that were, the selection among alternatives was of those procedures which should be most foolproof on site, and these were worked out thoroughly while keeping to minimum cost and, particularly, minimum site resources.

226. The most important economy was undoubtedly produced by the new cable spinning machinery. The use of this simple equipment should enable suspension bridges with parallel wire cables to be economical for spans well below recently considered limits, as well as being ideal for the longest spans.

227. The Authors of Part I have drawn attention to the change in the method of splicing the stiffening troughs between deck sections when compared with that used on the Severn Bridge. I should like to enlarge on the effects of this on erection.

228. I agree that omitting the tight fit of the trough end against the neighbouring section diaphragm gave an appreciable advantage in the operation of assembling sections. It did, however, add to the work of welding up the transverse joints between the sections on the bridge. Any discrepancies in the trough cross-section or alignment had to be dealt with at this stage by appropriate modifications to the short splice pieces and the amount of positional welding was about three times that required by the Severn detail. A further effect was that the heavy axial loads in the top flange between sections, which are an inevitable feature of progressive erection of a suspended deck, would be

DISCUSSION

taken by the projecting and prepared deck plate edge rather than by the troughs butting directly together. Such special measures as appeared feasible were taken to provide reinforcement points, but these were not entirely successful in avoiding distortion or damage to the deck plate edges and caused interruptions to the welding cycle. Nevertheless, I consider that subject to further study of this particular problem, the new detail probably remains an overall improvement.

229. The rate which can be achieved in assembling the welded deck sections has a major effect on the construction cost. Quite slow rates can be used, but only with a very early start and with provision for storing a very large number of sections before erection; the investment, of no future value, in the land and facilities for this is considerable.

230. At Severn, the average rate of assembly was 19 working days for a pair of sections off one stallage, with a single optimum of 15 days. At Bosporus, the average cycle for the larger sections, over two-thirds of the total assembly, was 12 working days, the best cycle being 9 days. The care taken to achieve accurate fabrication and the new and very economical seam welding method were major factors in this. But there is need to improve the rate still further.

Mr K. E. Hyatt, Consultant

I should mention that, by special arrangement, I was the resident engineer for Freeman Fox and Partners on this project for the first part of the work until October 1971. From that time Dr Brown was resident on the site. My knowledge is, therefore, concerned only with the first part of the work. My references to other projects are based on my experience on the Contractors' side, as board member, agent or consultant, and not as a member of the staff of Freeman Fox and Partners.

232. It is interesting to note that no tenders were received for the alternative truss design. Clearly, the break-through signalled by the Severn Bridge will persist, at any rate for single deck bridges. Incidentally, the Salazar Bridge was an American design and built by an American contractor.

233. With regard to cables, it is a pity in some ways that the preformed parallel wire strands proved unpopular, as experiments have been carried out on this system since the days of the Newport Bridge in the USA, and it would have been interesting to have tried again. However, with the clear refinements introduced by the Contractors, the spinning system would have taken a lot of beating on any job of any size.

234. The arrangement of the base sections on the towers was an improvement on the Severn arrangements so far as the holding down anchorage was concerned. The question of tolerances on the deck is a little more debatable, although the same general idea was reasonably successful at Severn. The construction of the foundations is not dealt with in detail. One is often in trouble when digging holes in the ground, and this was certainly the case at Bosporus. The complete system of borings did not give a true picture of all that lay beneath the surface, particularly on the Ortaköy site. As the ground was opened up, the rock was found to be folded and fissured with layers of soft material, and further borings and test holes had to be done as work proceeded. Vertical sides had to be held by rock-bolting and a considerable amount of redesign was necessary. The London office of the Consultants carried this out at speed and the Contractors, Hochtief AG, also did a fine job in pressing on undismayed through all the difficulties.

235. Foundation levels had to be lowered by up to 10 m and extra weight was added at selected points in the anchorages on both sides of the straits. The pier bases had to be deepened from 3 to $7\frac{1}{2}$ m and in some cases enlarged: extra borings were made, not only where there had been previous obstructions as at Ortaköy, but also off-shore, to test rock inclination and dip. It was clearly a wise decision to build the piers on shore. The seriousness of the situation is indicated by the galaxy of talent called to the site from the Royal School of Mines, Imperial College, and three months of extra construc-

70

tion time were definitely due to delay on the foundations. An account of this work would have been of great interest.

236. Turning to Part II, I should like to congratulate the Author on his very detailed account. The comparisons with Severn Bridge are most interesting. So far as the lifting of sections is concerned, lifting at Severn was only possible during two periods per month, and I always expected that the period could be halved in less tidal waters, which approximates to the time taken at Bosporus for the main span. In fact, at Severn two boxes were successfully lifted on one tide as an experiment, but the speed of assembly and launching made this impracticable as a general rule.

237. The arranging of fabrication from various shops in Italy and the United Kingdom was no mean task and worked surprisingly well. The differences in fabrication methods employed are interesting in view of difficulties being experienced in some shops in the UK for similar work. In view of the lack of space on site, and the size of pieces to be handled, particularly for the towers, the Contractors were fortunate that it was possible to find storage space in the docks through the good offices of the Turkish Directorate of Highways after the job had been started.

238. So far as cable spinning is concerned, the standard American method has been refined considerably over a sequence of jobs, whilst the basic principles, as stated, have been retained. Corners were cut, with savings of manpower on Severn and Quebec, but the new combination of reeling and unreeling was a striking advance of a different order, and must have resulted in very considerable economies. The lack of working space at this site alone would have made separate reeling and handling a tiresome operation. The signalling system took a stage further the changes made at Severn.

239. The cable wire requirements mentioned in §§ 117–119 are important. At Forth and Severn the wire drawing methods were satisfactory, particularly in the height from the galvanizing bath to the upper take-off sheaves and their diameter, but the importance of these methods was underlined by certain troubles at Quebec Bridge. Here also the smaller coils of 800 lb were more satisfactory than those of 1600 lb.

240. The failure of the tram rope splices is baffling in view of past experience. The same man made them for Forth, Severn and Bosporus. However, one can understand the difficulties in adjusting these large strands when compared with work at Severn where jacking loads were greater than expected with strands of 438 wires. The smaller void ratios after compaction are surprising, although it is interesting to note that the finished diameter of the Quebec cables was less than expected by the engineers, with consequent complications at the mid-span cable bands.

241. The remarks about deck fabrication and assembly are noted with interest. The flatness of deck plates will always be a problem and the matching of diaphragms for this shape of structure is still liable to give trouble in spite of improvements based on past experience. I feel that however much care is taken in fabrication for this type of welded box, its thin plating and non-rectangular structure make it very doubtful if the accuracy of the shop dimensions can ever match that of truss fabrication. Site assembly also makes for further small inaccuracies, although these are unimportant provided that the boxes match each other. This means, of course, that boxes must be assembled against each other in proper sequence.

242. The speed of assembly achieved at Bosporus was very creditable indeed, at least down to a 10 day cycle, and I would congratulate the Contractors on their solution to the welding problem. This must have saved a lot of time compared with this work at Severn. The method of moving and controlling the sections on the water was the fruit of much thought and experiment at Severn, and it is good to know that it has been successfully repeated at Bosporus as it was at Quebec.

243. I would now agree that barging is to be preferred to floating sections in the water. Painting troubles were persistent at Severn, and the necessary extra diaphragms have proved an unexpected nuisance with the bridge in service, owing to the unequal spacing and consequent hard spots on the deck. It would, however, have been difficult to use barges at Severn owing to the configuration of the banks of the River Wye and

lack of storage space. Two-point lifting was adopted at Severn to save time in making the attachments to the tackles. It was very quick but clearly not worth the extra complications.

244. As to viaduct erection, it had been thought that, since the viaducts were not suspended, this might have taken place before erection of the main span, but the configuration of the ground and its steep slope with difficult access would have made this laborious and expensive. I am not surprised that the main cables were distorted during erection. There was the same trouble after the small use that was made of this method at Severn. It would be very difficult to avoid, even with redesigned rollers, and I am glad to learn that recompaction was easy.

245. On the question of labour, I should like to endorse the remarks about Turkish labour. After some arguments and settlement with the union in the early days of the foundation work, the men worked very well indeed. It is a matter of interest that the apparently complicated work of cable spinning can readily be organized with untrained labour. Entirely fresh squads were also trained at Forth, Severn and Quebec with good results. Welding is a skill that seems to do well in foreign parts, as I have found in the past in such widely separated areas as Portugal, Africa and Asia.

Mr D. C. C. Dixon, Cleveland Bridge and Engineering Co. Ltd.

Great care was taken to ensure dimensional accuracy in the fabrication of the panels both for the towers and for the suspended structure. When such panels arrive on a site and fit is not as good as it should be, there is invariably a cry that the cause lies in the relaxation of residual stresses. It would be interesting to know if any such dimensional change was noticed on this bridge.

247. Since John A. Roebling spun the cables on Brooklyn Bridge in 1886 most engineers concerned with the construction of parallel wire cables have been convinced that there were simpler and cheaper systems which could be adopted. Because most of the systems envisaged involved radical change and hence considerable risk in the event of malfunction, no significant stride forward was made until the advances devised by Mr Knox. The new developments worked very well and it would be interesting to hear if there are further significant advances to be made and that the parallel strand method of construction can be economic over large spans.

248. Figure 21 shows a comparison between the programmes of construction for both the Severn and Bosporus Bridge, illustrating that Bosporus was not only constructed in a very much shorter time than the Severn, but in fact just 38 months after the start of work on the piers. Since the construction of the piers took some 4 months longer than the original programme time, effectively the bridge would have been completed in 34 months but for this factor. Tagus Bridge in Portugal by comparison took 51 months. One factor leading to this very successful result was undoubtedly that only one contractor was responsible for the whole of the superstructure, and thus there was none of the current almost inevitable 'decision by committee'. A small but highly qualified staff was able to cope with the many divergencies from what was inevitably a complex integrated programme in the first place.

Mr T. J. Upstone, Redpath Dorman Long (Contracting) Ltd.

I note that this orthotropic deck bridge is surfaced with 38 mm of asphalt surfacing. The same type of surfacing was used on the Severn Bridge built some eight years earlier. At the discussion on the Severn Bridge, I pointed out the considerable savings to be made in such large bridges by reducing the dead weight of the deck by using a much thinner epoxy surfacing. Sir Gilbert Roberts agreed with my comments at the time, and it is disappointing that the opportunity has not so far been taken to utilize epoxy surfacings with their considerable economy. Such surfacings have been developed and are available.

250. The cables for the Bosporus were designed for the tender as prefabricated

Fig. 40. Making prefabricated parallel strands

parallel wire strands. Although this was changed for the contract to conventional wire spinning, I consider prefabricated parallel strand could be used with economies for bridges of this size. Each cable of the Kammon Bridge in Japan with its 712 m main span was constructed of 154 prefabricated parallel wire strands each of 91 wires 5 mm in diameter. It is time British engineers had the opportunity to use this construction form; with such experience the advantages of using parallel wire strands could be properly assessed.

251. Experiments carried out last year in the UK have improved the methods of making parallel strands. Fig. 40 shows a set up for making such strands from coils of wire. The strands can be reeled for transport to the bridge site. Strands made by this process are suitable for use in cable stayed bridges as well as suspension bridges.

252. The Paper describes a new form of welded butt joint in plates, where the conventional rectangular backing strip is replaced by a specially shaped backing bar. In addition to the disadvantages quoted in the Paper, when used on orthotropic decks the conventional backing bar constitutes a very serious fatigue hazard. The new backing bar is deceptive, as externally it looks like a weld bead: in fact the bar is not completely fused into the plates but only attached to them where the weld penetrates along its centre line. It is possible to insert feeler gauges between the bar and the plate surface on each side of the bar. This constitutes a severe stress raiser where the butt weld penetrates into the backing bar.

253. Figure 41 shows how wheels rolling along the deck will produce a high number of stress fluctuations. The stress from wheels in position A can be as high as 100 N/mm^2 in tension with a 50 kN wheel. The stress levels will be greatly increased by the stress raiser in the new backing bar and consequently this detail could be a fatigue risk. The same detail is being used at Humber Bridge and I should like to ask the Authors what is its calculated fatigue life, and has this been proved by tests.

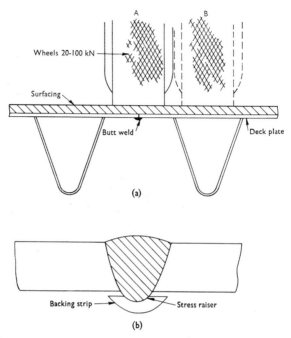

Fig. 41. (a) Section through deck ; (b) deck butt welded joint

254. The aerodynamic stability of the bridge was checked using uniform flow wind tunnels. What are the Author's views on the use of turbulent wind tunnels for such work? I believe boundary layer wind tunnel facilities do exist in the UK but am not aware that they have been used to any great extent for the testing of bridges and other similar structures.

Mr C. D. Brown, Mott Hay and Anderson

If the Bosporus Bridge were to be started now, I suspect that concrete towers would be used. In the early 1960s at the Tamar Bridge the indications were that concrete towers would be half the cost of steel towers. The Authors' firms are constructing very elegant concrete towers at the Humber Bridge. The advantages seem to me to be obvious: the use of indigenous materials, largely nominal reinforcement, flexible towers, and certainly no problems of local instability. I wonder whether the Bosporus suspension bridge may be the last major suspension bridge with steel towers. Have the Authors made comparisons of time and cost, as these would be helpful?

256. I should also like to comment on inclined suspenders and question their use. Ostenfeld[7] did not provide them for his welded box girders on the Lillebaelt suspension bridge and I am frankly sceptical that much energy is stored in practice by inclined hangers. Furthermore I presume that these dampers were manufactured in the short lay ($7\frac{1}{2}$ times the diameter) and there is accumulating evidence that there is undoubtedly creep with this type of hanger or this type of rope construction. Therefore, unless it is really necessary to use hangers as dampers, I would prefer much longer lay lengths. I do not think it makes much difference in a suspension bridge such as the Bosporus, but it may make some difference with long-term rope creep if hangers or main cables are used as dampers in a cable stay bridge.

257. Mr Upstone referred to the orthotropic deck construction and also to the fatigue problems with this type of deck. I would very much value some more details of the Authors' thinking on this. I certainly do not go along with Mr Upstone's suggestion at this stage that the asphalt thickness can be reduced, because clearly this is a material factor in improving the fatigue life of the deck. But more details of the deck and the Authors' thinking on fatigue life, and perhaps an estimate of the fatigue life that they anticipate for a Bosporus deck with asphalt surfacing, would be helpful.

258. There are at least two references in the Paper to checks under the Merrison rules for box girders, Dr Brown has suggested that the Merrison rules may not be of great value. The tower plate measurements indicate low deformations. Were these checks and measurements carried out after the erection and loading of the towers?

259. There is also reference to the modifications in the approach viaducts to meet the Merrison requirements, but no reference to any modifications to the towers. This may be part of Dr Brown's rebuttal of the Merrison rules, but I would have expected the towers to be much more affected by the rules than the approach viaducts. There is a clear inference that the Merrison rules have at best been selectively applied or perhaps even rejected. I support the selective approach to these rules. For example, in the case of the main box girder deck, the application of the Merrison rules is, in my opinion, unnecessary. It leads to considerable expense in design, and to heavy penalties on the cost of fabrication, which can give inequitable comparisons with other forms of construction. But bearing in mind that this is post Merrison, so that all may learn for the future, it would be of value if the Authors would develop further the yardsticks which they would utilize nowadays for various parts of the suspension bridge structure, bearing in mind the impact of the Merrison rules.

Mr P. Elliott, Department of the Environment

I have some questions to put to the Authors of Part I. The first relates to the aerodynamic stability. I noted in the comparative diagram of the suspension bridges the Bosporus is the only straight backstay bridge. All the others have suspended spans. The Authors state in § 33 that the NPL tests at Teddington showed flutter instability occurring well above the designed wind speed, which I think was 45 m/s at deck level and 51 m/s at the top of the tower. As I recall, the tests at Severn gave more than one critical wind speed, one of which was at a very low wind velocity of about 11 m/s, as well as other critical speeds at higher velocities. I should like to ask whether this apparent difference in aerodynamic response is caused by the absence of the suspended side spans, which the Authors state add to the stiffness of the centre span.

261. The second question deals with structural response in the aerodynamic mode. In view of the increased stiffness imparted by the straight backstays, do the Authors think there is continued justification for the inclined suspenders, and how much do these inclined suspenders contribute to the structural damping?

262. There is a reference in Part II to the use of Grade 50 B steel for the towers and 50 C for the deck. I should like to know whether it was dictated by availability of the steel, or whether it was a design requirement.

263. In his introduction Dr Brown referred to the sinusoidal mode of behaviour of compression panels. He suggested that these were not in accordance with observations on the Bosporus where, as the Paper shows, there was a cusping mode of deformation rather than the more adverse sinusoidal one. My comment on this is that Merrison was postulating the sinusoidal mode as that which was most likely to occur in the ultimate collapse state; even though panels would in practice show the cusping mode, when subjected to loads near the ultimate they might snap through from the cusping mode into the more adverse sinusoidal model Therefore, the Merrison rules merely say that it is safer to assume the sinusoidal mode of failure in the ultimate condition. This snapped through condition has been borne out by the very numerous tests which have been carried out in connexion with the Merrison programme.

DISCUSSION

Sir Ralph Freeman, Freeman Fox and Partners

Mr Upstone suggested that it was about time British engineers built a suspension bridge with preformed strands. That was in fact done by Mr Upstone's firm before World War II in Rhodesia.

265. Reference has been made to the fact that Bosporus bridge has straight backstays. That same bridge in Rhodesia for very similar reasons has straight backstays.

Mr F. N. Dinsdale, Cleveland Bridge and Engineering Co. Ltd.

My association with the Bosporus Bridge was in the capacity of Site Manager for the Cleveland Bridge and Engineering Co Ltd.

267. There were very exceptional reasons for attempting a record effort on the construction performance. There was massive increase in the need for a bridge of this type in Turkey during the 1960s; there was the very large revenue which would be realized from tolls, and there was the extreme political importance to the Turks of completing before the 50th Anniversary of the Turkish Republic towards the end of 1973. Under these conditions it was essential that the contract programme should be the right one to suit all the circumstances.

268. It is probable in retrospect that the political consideration might well have been the most important, and if it was, the contract programme could well have been extended by perhaps 6 months and still have achieved its objective. It was possible to make very accurate theoretical assessments of the best possible Bosporus construction time by virtue of the very good records deriving from the Severn Bridge experience, making allowance where necessary for design changes and for improved techniques. This exercise showed that under ideal working conditions the stipulated programme might just have been achieved. This is certainly consistent with the remarks in Part I that the programme 'whilst not unreasonable, required good fortune and few exceptional difficulties'. I find it difficult to reconcile the description of 'not unreasonable' when applied to a programme which at the same time required good fortune in order to implement it.

269. It was necessary in order to meet the superstructure programme in a largely unknown environment to clip about 15 or 16 months from the Severn programme. This was in fact done. The savings achieved were briefly 2 months in cable erection, 5 months in main span erection and welding, 6 months in approach span erection, and 2 months in surfacing. All these stages were carried out at near the optimum speeds, as estimated, after allowances were made for the times at which good fortune, alas, deserted us. Two such occasions are referred to in the Paper: one was the damage beyond repair of the main portal panel during off-loading, which had to be replaced from Italy in a period of 1 month, and the loss of six main viaduct boxes into 6 m of murky Marmara Sea due to an unprecedented storm. This could have added many months to the programme had it not been that the amount of damage that was done was small, and of course that we were able to find them. There were other incidents, for example the damage beyond repair of 600 m of bond rope on one of the tower cranes. It was necessary to air freight a rope from England and the crane was out of commission for 6 weeks.

270. Taken separately, and with a more normal contract programme, all such incidents could be handled with reasonable economy. Taken however in the context of a programme where time is of utmost importance, the contractor is forced into measures which involve excessive costs which are quite disproportionate to the value he may recover.

271. I would suggest that where there are exceptional conditions such as that of an extraordinary requirement for speed, a form of contract which carried a bonus element would have been appropriate. Had that been done, the formal contract period could have been extended by six months to give protection against normal contingencies and still at the very worst have reflected a good performance by any standards. If it was then felt that some further time saving was possible, either from the absence of unforeseen difficulties or the method of dealing with them when they arose, then the anticipated

Fig. 42. Humber
Bridge : construction
of anchorage, south
bank

revenue of perhaps £250 000/month which would accrue from opening the bridge could
surely have provided one half of that per month as a bonus to the contractor for earlier
completion, thereby of course encouraging him to do so whilst at the same time re-
imbursing to him the high cost of acceleration when dealing with unforeseen conditions.

Mr B. Wex, Freeman Fox and Partners

In § 26 the Authors mention the question of the employment of concrete or steel for
the Bosporus towers and their decision that, because of earthquakes and speed of construction required, steel should be used.   Mr C. D. Brown has observed that on the
Humber Bridge the design uses concrete, and he sees some apparent contradiction.
Freeman Fox have known for a very long time that a concrete tower is basically considerably cheaper to construct that one of steel, but when the 'rent' comes from toll
revenue, it is important to get the bridge structure completed as soon as possible.   For
this reason my firm has heretofore favoured steel.   However, there have been considerable advances in slip forming concrete and we felt very strongly that with slip
forming, concrete construction for the Humber Bridge towers could rival or reduce the
construction time taken by steel in current UK conditions.   This, in conjunction with
the fact that the first cost of the tower was certainly much lower led to the employment of
the concrete form of construction.

273. In § 18, the Authors describe their decision to move the foundation from the water onto the edge of the Bosporus. Fig. 42 epitomises the trouble which can arise when constructing in water. At Humber, the north tower was complete whilst there were still difficulties in constructing the foundations on the south side. The delays had nothing to do with the use of concrete for the tower and were entirely due to the fact that the foundations were being constructed in tidal water in very difficult ground with considerable problems attached to it. This is proof of the Authors' wisdom in deciding to put the foundations of the Bosporus Bridge on dry land. Unfortunately, to have done the same at Humber would have added more thn 500 m to the main span.

274. Questions have been raised by Mr Upstone about the deck and fatigue. He has talked about square backing bars and half round backing bars. My firm has used square backing bars on other bridges and has done fatigue analysis on those bridge decks. The square backing bar, if put in the proper place and continuously fillet welded, is not the critical detail. If there is a fatigue problem it is in the welds joining the troughs to the deck plate. Mr Upstone would substitute a thin layer of epoxy resin for the deck surfacing in place of the thicker mastic asphalt but this, by load spreading and composite action with the steel deck, very considerably relieves the flexural stresses therein. Thus, by substituting a thinner layer of deck surfacing, fatigue of the deck plate itself might well become a problem.

Mr B. G. Blakeley, Cleveland Bridge and Engineering Co. Ltd.

Both Mr Knox and Mr Hyatt have mentioned the quality of the labour. Although the men were recruited locally in Istanbul, for the most part they came from the towns and villages of Anatolia. They had a variety of skills, but very few had ever seen, let alone taken part in, heavy erection work. However, their willingness to work and to learn more than made up for their lack of knowledge.

276. The basic working week was 48 h for $5\frac{1}{2}$ days, with some selective overtime for critical activities. In general it was found desirable to avoid working on Sunday which was the official day of rest in Turkey. Apart from the shift arrangements during the cable spinning period, it was also necessary to place the cable wrapping on a two-shift basis to obtain the maximum advantage from the available summer daylight hours.

277. Mr Dinsdale has mentioned the near catastrophe due to a sudden storm in the Marmara, and this of course illustrates that weather conditions are always a major factor in maintaining progress. Although Istanbul is a place with something of a reputation for strong winds and bad weather, conditions were generally a good deal better than could be expected in the UK.

278. In tightening the cable band bolts there was a significant departure from the method adopted on the Severn Bridge where the bolts were tensioned to just below the elastic limit, and maintained at that load until given a final half-turn of the nut after wrapping. This time on the Bosporus Bridge, having taken all the bolts up to just below the elastic limit on the first round of tightening, they were given a further full turn of the nut. It seems to have been assumed that this would produce a further extension of 2 mm to match the pitch of the threads. In practice only 1 mm of bolt extension was obtained. The remainder could be accounted for equally I believe between further compaction of the cable and some thread distortion.

279. In carrying out the final pass after wrapping, when an additional half-turn of the nut was specified, it was found that the nuts in many cases had seized up completely. Fortunately bolts and nuts had been over-supplied by the manufacturers: otherwise there would have been insufficient replacements available.

280. The reasons for specifying the full turn of the nut so early in the tensioning sequence were never clear to me. I do not believe that the additional load involved could have had any significance in cutting down on the relaxation effects, or on the number of passes which had to be made for each tensioning. I would welcome some clarification of the reasoning which led to this method of tightening.

Dr O. A. Kerensky, Consultant, Freeman Fox and Partners

I am not speaking for the designer, but as Chairman of British Standard Committee 116 which is drafting the specification for bridges in steel and concrete. I have four points to make.

282. When the Bosporus Bridge was being checked, it was checked by appraisal rules. Since then the B116 Committee has been working on Merrison, and what will be produced will be less conservative and easier to apply. I am quite certain of that.

283. Secondly, the test results that Dr Brown mentioned were communicated to the Committee, and the Committee's scientists were aware of these tests.

284. Coming back to Mr Upstone's question concerning the question of epoxy, epoxy resin has never been approved by the Transport and Road Research Laboratory. All the tests failed in durability, and the composite action of asphalt on steel multiplies the life of the bridge by about ten, which is a very significant feature.

285. Finally, the fatigue of backing strips is not due to the butt weld weakness, but to the fact that when ordinary backing strips were used, there were intermittent fillet welds and they were classified as of very low fatigue strengths; the other backing welds are therefore better whatever the butt weld itself.

Mr R. B. Hill, Cleveland Bridge and Engineering Co. Ltd.

This question of asphalt really needs a few more words. Mr Upstone knows that his firm and Cleveland Bridge have recently had experience of an epoxy asphalt deck on a major bridge which, if it has not failed, is very near to it. A great deal more research and investigation need to be done before anything other than hand-laid mastic asphalt, such as was used at Bosporus, can be accepted by engineers as a satisfactory wearing course direct on steel decks.

287. There are of course, potential difficulties to be considered with hand-laid asphalt. One of my most vivid memories of Bosporus Bridge was the problem of laying the mastic in time for the opening to suit the 50th Anniversary of the Kemal Attaturk revolution in October 1973, when only 13 weeks were available for the operation. There are only two firms in Europe, one in Germany and one in Britain, who could undertake the work, there being only 20 or 30 men left in the world who can hand lay mastic asphalt. I am glad to say that the British firm was chosen and completed the work satisfactorily on time.

Mr A. M. Muir Wood, Sir William Halcrow and Partners

While expressing admiration for the elegant design of the visible part of this bridge, I am disappointed in the cursory way in which the pier foundations and anchorages are dismissed. I have the following questions to ask.

289. What was the nature and extent of site investigation? It appears that this went not much further than the determination of the surface of sound rock, and no doubt the tight programme prior to tender impeded a more thorough investigation. It would be interesting to know what the Authors feel should have been undertaken in this respect and the factors taken into account in the additional excavation undertaken for one or more piers.

290. It has been suggested that the anchorage design was based upon an ultimate ground loading condition. Could not greater benefit have been derived from the favourable arrangement of cables to make greater use of passive loading of the rock to the front and sides of each anchorage, recognizing that this would depend considerably upon the different ground conditions for the two anchorages.

291. Have records been made for the movement in load of the anchorages and piers and, if so, can these be related to the nature of the ground and to the extent and nature of the jointing of the rock?

292. Brief mention was given concerning the extent of minimum depth of pier foundation for stability, presumably in the temporary works condition. Was consideration

DISCUSSION

given to the use of ground anchors either to reduce this excavation or for the anchor blocks?

Mr R. J. Bridle, Department of the Environment

The tests referred to by Dr Brown were those carried out in 1972 by Dr Nelson at Glasgow University. They were commissioned by the Department of the Environment at the suggestion of Freeman Fox and Partners at a time when the B116/6 Committee was considering drafts of the Merrison interim design rules, and also the results of an extensive series of box girder tests carried out as part of the Merrison programme. Three boxes were tested at Glasgow. The test specimens were box crane beams surplus to requirements. As manufactured, the flange plates were too stiff for a flange induced failure to be attained with the test facilities available. To overcome this the boxes were turned on their sides and the web plates, with stiffeners added, became the flanges for the purpose of the tests. The boxes failed in flexure. The test results were analysed by Freeman Fox and the conclusions drawn by Dr Brown were derived from that analysis.

294. The Merrison Committee also studied the Glasgow results but said they had reservations over the conclusions. One unresolved problem was that of flange/web interaction in estimating the contribution of the over-stiff web plates, manufactured as flanges, to the ultimate flexural strength recorded under test. The Merrison Committee decided that owing to lack of time in which to complete the report ready for presentation to the Secretary of State, it could not investigate these tests further and also concluded that it could not adopt results which were uncharacteristic of many others which had previously been analysed in greater depth for use as a basis for the Merrison interim design rules. Since then, no final report of the tests has yet been received and no further analysis of the results has been carried out.

295. Having quoted the Glasgow results in support of his assertion that the Merrison rules are very conservative Dr Brown elevates these tests to a level of importance commensurate with that of the Bosporus Bridge. The DoE will accordingly arrange for the test results to be re-examined and will seek to obtain further information which will enable comparison to be made with predictions made from the Merrison rules. This will take some time to complete. When results are available they will be made available to Dr Brown and will be offered for publication.

296. The Severn Bridge towers, designed and built before Merrison in accordance with BS 153, have recently been subjected to an independent Merrison appraisal for the DoE and were found just to comply without need for added stiffening. It would therefore be relevant to learn whether the Authors regard the Severn towers as conservatively designed.

Mr D. W. Smith, University of Dundee

Only once in history can any two continents first become joined by a permanent bridge. Designers and builders have produced, in a remarkably short time, a splendid structure worthy of this unique occasion. The Freeman Fox box form of suspended structure has been finally vindicated, if vindication were necessary, by the absence of takers for the alternative lattice form. This is particularly interesting in view of the advanced version of this lattice form, incorporating the steel deck as the top chord of the stiffening truss. Can the Authors say whether any existing major truss-stiffened suspension bridge exhibits this feature? How much steel was saved, in the alternative design, by using the deck in this way?

298. It is useful to have the point explicitly made, in § 43, that a large suspension bridge does not require stiffening from the suspended structure other than for aerodynamic reasons. Was there a good reason against reducing the shallow depth even further, say to 2 m, which would have been $\frac{1}{14}$th of the transverse span between hangers? Would this have been too shallow to allow separation of the natural frequencies in bending and torsion?

299. It would also be interesting to hear the Authors expand further on the need or otherwise for sloping hangers. They are a pleasing feature, and perhaps a prudent last line of defence against overall bridge oscillation: but the Lillebaelt Bridge appears to be successful without them, and the conventional four-part vertical hanger lends itself more readily to inhibiting aerodynamic oscillation of the hangars themselves.

300. In § 47 it is pointed out that mastic asphalt, laid by hand, is not perfect, but is the best surfacing currently available for a steel deck. It would be interesting to learn the Authors' views as to likely or desirable future development. Should the aim be to improve riding qualities by laying mastic asphalt by machine, or to produce an alternative material that can be laid thinner so as to save weight? Can a steel deck be made flat enough for a satisfactory road surface to be made with less than 38 mm of surfacing? Would this involve an unacceptable loss in fatigue protection to the steelwork?

301. It is surprising that conventional cable spinning showed a large saving in cost compared with the use of prefabricated strands (§ 90). Would this, in the Authors' opinion, apply to all sites, or would the reverse be true under colder and windier conditions? Was the availability of existing equipment an important term in this cost equation?

Mr B. Birdsall, Partner, Steinman Boynton Gronquist and London, New York

The design and construction of the Bosporus Bridge represent a continuation of the outstanding creative thinking which has been originating in England since the 1950s and the profession is indebted to the Authors for the fine description of these developments contained in this Paper and the corresponding opportunity to discuss their merits.

303. The following comments deal with § 25 of the Paper. The first sentence makes the unqualified statement that parallel wires have greater efficiency than prefabricated spiral strands. In my experience, it may be said that this statement, while technically correct, is not true to the extent normally assumed. The actual strength of a prefabricated spiral wire strand of conventional design is, for all practical purposes, identical to that of a strand made up of the very same wires laid parallel to each other. There is a slight difference in modulus of elasticity and there is, for the prefabricated spiral strands, the disadvantage that cable bands and saddles must be larger for a cable of the same total wire area. This has been discussed in more detail elsewhere.[8]

304. In the same paragraph appears the phrase that '. . . the aerial spinning technique was available from only a few possible contracting companies . . .' This implies that the alternative, i.e. prefabricated parallel wire strands, would be available from a much wider range of contracting companies. In my opinion, this is not a foregone conclusion. The production of prefabricated parallel wire strand requires a carefully engineered and expensive special set-up and not every contractor would have available to him the necessary expertise. However, there are many elements of cost which enter into the choice between the aerial spinning technique and that of prefabricated parallel wire strands, some in favour of one and some in favour of the other, and the relative advantages will vary depending on the individual contractor, the geographic area in which the work is to be done, etc.

305. In § 28 appears the statement 'a modified BS153-HA loading was adopted . . .' but the modifications are not stated. I presume that the test loading stated in § 80 gives an indication of the degree of modification of the above standard loading. However, a clearer statement would be in order for the record.

306. With respect to § 33, would it be in order to ask for a statement of the assumed logarithmic decrement for this type of structure both with and without the diagonal suspenders?

307. I am somewhat confused when comparing § 46 with §§ 123, 188 and 189. On the one hand, the text appears to say that the floor system was designed for ease of fabrication and a minimum need for tolerances. On the other it states that tight tolerances were required and fabrication was not particularly easy. Probably some of my difficulty lies in the terminology and I trust that clarification can be included in the reply.

DISCUSSION

308. I would also request a clarification of the last sentence of § 52. Would the following wording 'There are close tolerance locating bolts at the ends of each panel. However, these are not counted on to take shear. All the shear forces are carried through friction by waisted grip bolts . . .' have the same meaning?

309. The additional specifications outlined in §§ 118 and 119 were indeed very important to the achievement of the proper quality of wire for the benefit of a manufacturer who has not previously had the experience of manufacturing wire for this service. I would like to emphasize also the importance of including in the basic specifications, as is done in Table 8, an upper limit for tensile strength. This also is for the benefit of manufacturers not previously experienced in this product.

310. In my view, the basic innovation in the construction of the cables is described in § 166. It is the extremely high speed of reeling which was achieved. That this could be done successfully without snagging or kinking the wire indicates a new excellence in the preparation of the coils and in the design of the swifts and their operating methods. Given this basic innovation, the procedures described in § 163 represent a more or less natural development on the part of a contractor endowed with creative thinking. With nothing more to go on but the texts and photographs published in the Paper, I was at first puzzled as to how the described machinery could achieve the stated results. However reading between the lines, I recognized that the secret must lie in an arrangement which is not clearly described in the text. Apparently, each of the two reels of a pair was driven independently and could therefore operate at a speed, and even in a direction, completely independent of those of its neighbouring reel. This recognition also erased another question mark in my mind. With this arrangement it does appear that there would be enough time, in the reeling operation, to permit the normal amount of sampling of wire splices to maintain the necessary continuous control of the condition of the splicing dies and of splicing techniques.

311. I strongly recommend that no engineer or contractor seize hastily on these innovations as an easy way to reduce costs or increase profits. Their success in this case was the result not only of experience on several structures, but also through several generations of creative practitioners, all working in continuity toward the same goal: maximum quality at minimum cost.

312. The experience described in § 170 regarding troubles with the hauling rope splices, is indeed interesting. I do not find in the text a statement of the size of the hauling rope. From the published data, I also agree that the trouble must have come from the combination of circumstances but I do not quite understand why the length of the splice was necessarily restricted or the tension in the rope necessarily high.

313. The last sentence in § 172 states 'It would seem that the strand size used here is close to the limit which is practicable with current methods of spinning in the saddles.' It seems to me that the experience described in § 172 effectively demonstrates that the strand size used here was beyond the limit which is practicable.

314. In § 175 (a) a relaxation on this project of the usual standards required in spinning is indicated. It appears clear from this description that wires at the top of a strand at the splay point are located at the bottom of the strand at the tower top. This would be at the beginning of the spinning of the strand. At the end of spinning, bottom wires at the splay point would be top wires at the tower saddle. This means that many of the wires in the strand make a 180° turn around the strand in proceeding from the splay point to the tower saddle. Previously, this condition has been studiously avoided in any section of cable which is to be compacted. Such a condition has always been confined to the splay of the strand.

315. The figures on compactness stated in § 178 may be seen in perspective by comparison with those for several other bridges which have been published elsewhere.[4] Corresponding to the 22·2% voids stated in the Paper, the voids at Golden Gate, first Tacoma, second Tacoma and Forth Road were respectively 19·4, 20·2, 19·8 and 21·7. Forth Road was greater than the first three because of the storm-induced aberrations and the result at Bosporus might well be due to the comparatively larger strand size. The

corresponding figure for the Pierre Laporte Bridge at Quebec is 21·6% which is very good indeed for the 'flat-topped hexagon' cable arrangement. From the meagre information provided in the Paper, it would appear that the mechanical efficiency of compacting was in the order of magnitude of the best. The pressure per wire seems a little high but this is probably due to the fact that the spacing between the applications of the compactor was apparently somewhat wider than normal.

316. Admittedly, the wrapping machines used at Forth and Severn were more expensive in fabrication and use than those used at Quebec and Bosporus. The historic rationale for the type of machine used at Forth and Severn was that the wrapping could be applied at a higher tension than needed for the completed bridge and that this would thus make it possible to wrap the cables earlier in the construction process than otherwise. I believe that the thought is still valid, but I also believe that there has never been a case when full advantage has been taken of this distinction. Thus, I have no reason to question the contractor's judgment in the case of Quebec and Bosporus.

317. The same cannot be said with respect to the subject of § 181. Here, I question the philosophy stated in the Paper. In the first place, I have never found anything detrimental to either the cost or quality of the wrapping in the small amount of out-of-roundness of the as-compacted cable referred to in the Paper as an 'elliptical shape'. The principal difference in philosophy has to do with the reasoning regarding the cable bands. Although the details of the cable bands on Bosporus are not included in the Paper, it is presumed that they are designed fundamentally as straps and not as rigid yokes. If the cable is compacted to a true circle, it follows that the diameter of this circle must be something larger than the diameter of a circle having an area equal to the final cross-sectional area of the cable within the cable bands. The designer would have two choices in determining the as-manufactured contour of the cable band halves: he could make them in the form of true semi-circles corresponding to the larger diameter mentioned above; alternatively, he could shape the cable band halves to his estimate of the ellipitical shape which the cable will take under the cable band. In either case, the as-manufactured opening of the cable band halves must be such as can be placed over the compacted cable.

318. In the first instance, the cable band will start out as two semi-circles and the initial contact surface between cable band and cable will have the same circular configuration. As pressure is applied, however, if all elements perform ideally, and assuming zero friction between cable band and wire, the forces produced by the cable band bolts will be uniformly radial and the situation will stabilize under full bolt tension at a circle of smaller diameter. This change in radius of curvature of the band necessarily brings with it a bending moment in the cable band. This bending moment might be of little consequence on a true strap but, even though the band be designed basically as a strap, there must unavoidably be stress raisers in the form of bolt housings and, in the case of many bridges, suspender grooves. This procedure would, therefore, necessarily lock in to the cable band some secondary stresses. If, as stated by the Authors, the end result is an elliptical shape, this would accentuate even more the moment-producing changes in angle.

319. If the bands are manufactured as half ellipses, the chain of events would be somewhat different but the results would be similar. All the forces applied by the cable against the cable band would be such as to attempt to make the cable band round. This interaction would at least cause some change in the initial curvature of the band which would in turn cause bending moments in the band·

320. Under either of the above conditions, there is nothing inherent in the situation which, during the life of the bridge would tend to relieve the secondary stresses, but would rather aggravate them.

321. Under the other philosophy, which is my preference, the cable is compacted to a diameter along the line between the openings of the cable band equal to the predicted final cable diameter within the cable band. This means that the diameter at 90° to this diameter is somewhat larger. The cable band bore is made to suit the expected diameter

DISCUSSION

of the cable in the finished bridge within the cable band. When the cable band first contacts the cable, the points of contact will be at the openings between the cable bands and on the diameter at 90° to the plane through the openings. As the bolts are tightened, there is an initial tendency to deflect the band to an elliptical shape. However, as the band pressure increases, the pressures of the cable against the cable band would become more and more nearly uniform and radial, tending to restore the cable band to its original circular shape. As long as the voids in the cable within the cable band are estimated closely but not overestimated, the tendency throughout the life of the structure will be either to achieve the original shape of the cable bands or to continually approach that shape, thereby always deforming in the direction of relieving any initial secondary bending stresses.

322. If the cable bands are conceived and designed as rigid yokes, the above refinements are of no consequence but one would expect the cable bands to be heavier and more costly than necessary.

Dr Brown and Mr Parsons

Mr Knox refers to the difficulties in transmitting a horizontal component of the inclined hanger loads during erection and suggests that the butting of the trough sections at Severn Bridge made for easier welding. Perhaps he should have mentioned also that the arrangement at Severn incorporated a large temporary buffer located along the centre line of the bridge and this was omitted at Bosporus.

324. Owing to the manner in which the deck sags during erection, most of this horizontal force is concentrated along the centre line and the lack of such a buffer meant that the deck plate had to sustain some of this force through the sloping weld preparations thus causing some plates to overlap.

325. The site seam welding was certainly speeded up by the use of automatic machines and must now be preferred over the hand welding originally suggested by his company. The welds might have been laid quicker, however, if such welding had been accepted at the outset and the edge preparations made accordingly. As it was, the preparations were those suitable for hand welding and this meant that a limit had to be placed on the electrode current and hence on speed of welding.

326. In reply to Mr Hyatt's contribution, as far as we could see neither the flatness of the plate nor the non-rectangular structure provided any difficulty. As explained in the Paper, provided boxes are matched to each other during assembly there is no particular requirement for absolute close tolerance manufacture. All that is required is for the method of manufacture to be consistent, and it is wasteful to work to tight tolerances. It is interesting to record therefore that although the Contractor supplied a mixture of 'wide' and 'narrow' panels, in fact many of the boxes were assembled from random panels near to hand with no detrimental effect.

327. Mr Upstone refers to the specially shaped backing bar used in the deck weld seams. The backing bars used at Severn Bridge were not entirely satisfactory. On that occasion it was necessary to turn the panels in the shops for attachment and thereafter dirt and grit were trapped between the bar and the plate during grit-blasting which later gave rise to porosity unless the welds were made in two runs. Because other methods of fixing the backing bar were possible, at the time of tender it was decided to leave the final arrangement to the Contractor. However, in the event, the Contractor was extremely keen to do all welding by hand and apart from other obvious difficulties time of operation was an important factor. The Contractor was therefore encouraged to carry out experiments using firstly water-cooled copper bars and then grooved carbon blocks. It was when these latter proved unsatisfactory that further thought was given to the use of steel bars and it was suggested to the Contractors that they might use a half round strip supported by a carbon block. However, apart from occasional burn-through, the cheaper steel backing blocks proved very satisfactory. An essential requirement is however that the plates are carefully levelled along the full length of the

joint. Failure to do so will mean that the backing strip cannot be held up tight and weld spillage results. It would seem that the defects shown by Mr Upstone might be caused by this or some other weakness in the weld procedure.

328. Mr Upstone referred to the possibility of using a much thinner surfacing of epoxy, and the advantages and disadvantages of this were discussed by several other speakers. Our opinion, in line with the consensus of the contributors to the discussion, is that insufficient information exists to warrant the use of a thin epoxy surfacing on an orthotropic steel deck as used for the Bosporus Bridge unless it can be applied under factory conditions. We consider that the most promising development is in the use of machine laid epoxy asphalt where some of the bitumen binder in mastic asphalt is replaced by epoxy. As a first step we would not try to achieve economy by reducing the thickness but would rather concentrate on obtaining the advantages of a smoother riding surface, a greatly reduced laying time, improved fatigue life for both the surfacing and the steel deck, and improved corrosion protection for the steel deck.

329. Regarding the suggestion that British engineers should be given the opportunity to use prefabricated wire strands, it was the intention to do just this when inviting tenders for the Bosporus Bridge, and indeed we have been accused by Mr Knox of giving an unfair advantage to this less conventional form of main cable construction.

330. Although from the fatigue aspect the detail of the site butt welds may not be ideal, it is, in our opinion, considerably better than the backing flat detail previously used. Furthermore, as pointed out by Mr Wex, this butt weld is not the critical fatigue detail in the deck.

331. Mr C. D. Brown suggests that if we were designing the Bosporus Bridge now concrete towers would be used. This is debatable, and the decision would partly depend on the time available for the design and the necessary investigation into the effect of earthquake on a concrete tower in both the erection and final conditions. As stated elsewhere in the discussion, we are aware of the direct economic advantages of a concrete tower in non-earthquake conditions. Even here, however, concrete towers are likely to take longer to construct and in some countries and climatic conditions would be subject to a greater degree of uncertainty with regard to both the quality control and construction time.

332. We do not consider that rope creep is a problem with the short lay length suspenders since the dead load stress is only a comparatively small percentage (18%) of the breaking load. We agree that short lay length strands should not be used for main cables, unless provision is made to correct long-term creep.

333. In reply to the query concerning the yardsticks we would utilize nowadays for the design of the various parts of a suspension bridge we would make the following points:

(a) the Bosporus Bridge, in common with all our major suspension bridges, has been designed using a stress factor method, i.e. basically to BS 153;

(b) this has led to a situation where, due to the high proportion of dead load, the towers and cables of these bridges have a much higher live load factor against collapse than the conventional 1·7–2·0; the deck structure on the other hand has a live load factor of only about 1·7 against local collapse.

In our opinion this greater live load factor for the main supporting elements is a beneficial consequence of using the stress factor method. This was forcibly brought home to us on the opening day of the Bosporus Bridge when we estimate that the crowd loading could have imposed a live load on the structure approximately equal to three times the design load. Since a local failure in the suspended structure cannot lead to collapse of the bridge we consider that the application of the same load factors to the deck as to the towers and cables would lead to a wasteful distribution of material. We agree with Mr Brown that the application of the Merrison rules to the suspended box is unnecessary.

334. In reply to Mr Elliott, the effect of the straight back stays on the aero-

dynamic behaviour of the Bosporus Bridge was to raise slightly the critical velocities, but otherwise it did not have any fundamental effect. The Bosporus Bridge aerodynamic model did exhibit signs of low amplitude single degree of freedom oscillations at low wind speeds of about 2 m/s for vertical and 6 m/s for torsional motion. However, even with a structural damping logarithmic decrement of only 0·014 the maximum amplitude was only 6·6 cm and when the log. decrement was increased to the expected 0·07 the single degree of freedom oscillations were eliminated. The predicted log. decrement without the inclined hangers was 0·02, and this was not quite enough to eliminate the oscillations.

335.   The use of Grade 50C for the deck plate and Grade 50B for the towers was a design requirement. We originally specified Grade 968 steel for the deck with impact tests and this is similar to Grade 50C. This was considered useful, especially in an international tender, to ensure that the quality of steel for the deck plate would not give any brittle cracking problems in the local zones of tensile stress. In the finished bridge the tower legs are always in compression and hence impact tests on the steel were not required.

336.   **Mr Bridle** and Mr Elliott refer to the tests on box girders and the Merrison rules. The first two of these tests were carried out at the Chepstow works of Messrs Fairfield-Mabey Ltd in July 1971, just after the first set of rules was issued.

337.   In his introduction to the discussion Dr Brown was careful to point out that he was referring to the use of Merrison rules in the ratio of both panel and plate normally used in practice, and in particular for the Bosporus Bridge approaches, i.e. those panels which carry stresses approaching the basic allowable values and are proportioned appropriately in accord with obvious accepted practice (mild steel, $b/t \ngtr 40$ and high yield steel $b/t \ngtr 35$ and l/r of longitudinal stiffeners between cross members about 40). The test specimens at Chepstow and Glasgow were therefore in this range, but additionally combined high shear and axial stress. The results of these and the later Glasgow tests demonstrated that the rules were conservative and that simpler methods of analysis produced more accurate results even when the plastic strength of the lower yield point webs were also taken into account. Since the Merrison rules appear to have been based on theoretical assumptions without experimental verification we would be very pleased to see the Committee's further comments on these tests, especially if at the same time they could comment on all other recent tests including those carried out by the DoE[9] and by Horne and Narayanan.[10] In our opinion all these confirm the contention that within the slenderness ratios mentioned above the rules are inappropriate (Tables 11 and 12).

338.   We agree with Mr Elliott that it might be possible for panels to 'snap' into a sinusoidal mode, but only if the slenderness ratio is so high that the theoretical critical stress is well below the yield point of the material. Such slenderness ratios have little practical significance. Similarly, one would expect test results on models incorporating such high ratios to provide reasonable agreement with a purely mathematical approach which incorporates irregularities since in that circumstance their effect is less important and can be exaggerated without causing great error. One would have to be cautious

Table 11. Chepstow tests : collapse conditions

Beam	Reaction, tons			SBG6A ÷ test
	Test result	Assuming full plasticity	SBG6A	
C1	83·3*	77	58·2	0·70
C2	94·1	77	58·2	0·63

* Web failure

in concluding that such experiments justified a similar approach to plates and panels having lower slenderness values.

339. In **Mr Dinsdale's** contribution he referred to our phrase that the contract programme required 'good fortune' and we would like to clarify this. The main eventuality we had in mind was that if unforeseen conditions in the ground for the foundations arose, these would lead to an extension of the contract period. We sympathize with Mr Dinsdale in that we probably did not allow sufficient time for the sort of difficulties he refers to in obtaining replacements for specialized items of equipment and plant in an overseas contract of this nature. Although his idea of a large bonus for early completion appears attractive, we must wonder whether the implementation of such a procedure would not lead to acrimonious argument concerning claims for extension of time.

340. **Mr Wex** refers to the use of concrete for the construction of the Humber Bridge towers and points out that the use of slip-form shuttering reduces the construction time of concrete towers and makes them more competitive relative to the use of steel. We agree with this, but as noted in our reply to Mr C. D. Brown, we consider that the choice of material for suspension bridge towers still has to be considered for each individual case.

341. **Mr Blakeley** requests reasons for the specified method of tightening cable band bolts on the Bosporus Bridge. The objective of the tightening procedure is to attempt to remove as much as possible of the bedding down of the cable during the erection stage so that when the bridge is complete the subsequent relaxation of the tension in the cable band bolts is kept to a minimum. We believe that the procedure specified for the Bosporus Bridge was in this respect an improvement over that adopted for the Severn, since a higher compacting force could be applied to the cable over the available erection period starting from the first tightening of the bolts.

342. We are glad to note with **Dr Kerensky** that the Merrison rules will never form part of a British Standard. If by that he means that any revisions to the present BS 153 will be based on those theories proven by practice and experiment, then we would have thought that for all practical purposes the present BS 153 is good enough.

343. We were concerned to hear from **Mr Hill** of the possible failure of the epoxy asphalt which had been used on a recent major bridge and trust that the cause of this failure will be made known so that it may be avoided in future applications of this promising development.

344. **Mr Muir Wood** comments on the initial site investigation and suggests that it appeared to be inadequate. In our opinion most site investigations prove to be 'inadequate', but in this case we and the Client's engineers did as much as possible in the time available. In addition to an investigation carried out for the 1960 D. B. Steinman design, a further investigation was carried out in 1968 to suit the location of the redesigned bridge. For this investigation six boreholes were drilled at the site of each of the anchorages, one in each corner and one in front of the line of each of the main cables. In addition six holes were sunk at the site of the Ortaköy pier and two

Table 12. Glasgow tests : collapse conditions

Beam	Reaction, tons			SBG6A ÷ test
	Test result	Assuming full plasticity	SBG6A	
TB20	88·6	80	66·6	0·75
TB21	99·4	92	75·5	0·76
TB22	131·9	121	94·3	0·71

at the Beylerbeyi pier. All the boreholes extended between 4·5 and 14 m below the designed founding level. Laboratory tests, consisting of unconfined compression tests and shear box tests on cut samples, were carried out on samples taken from the cores.

345. If more time had been available we would have arranged for trial pits to be dug at the initial stage so that the results of examining the rock could have been incorporated in the tender designs. However, we consider that in all the circumstances we were correct to design the foundations on the basis of the borehole results, making as we did reasonable assumptions about the possible existence of bands of zero cohesion. For example in the design of the anchorages, whilst we always assumed the existence of friction of the slip failure planes, we did not assume cohesive strength to exist on both the bases and the sides of the anchorage concurrently. In the event three of the four anchorage chambers were constructed essentially as originally designed and it was only in the west chamber of the Ortaköy anchorage where extensive modifications were made. In the original design passive loading on the front of the anchorages was allowed for and this was retained in the design for all except the west chamber of the Ortaköy anchorage. We have not been able to record any discernible movement of either anchorage.

346. Consideration was given to the use of ground anchors but the rock on both sides of the Bosporus was so shattered that it was considered essential for the engineers to see the rock around each foundation.

347. In reply to **Mr Smith** we are not aware of any existing major suspension bridge where a steel deck is incorporated as part of the top cord of the stiffening truss as proposed in our alternative for the Bosporus Bridge. It is difficult to say how much steel was saved by this innovation, but if the deck were to be made independent from the truss and the same stiffness were to be maintained, we would estimate the required increase in steel would be of the order of 10%. Apart from the saving of steel, however, the advantage of the integral deck design was that the necessity for expansion joints in the deck was eliminated. This simplifies the maintenance requirements and improves the riding quality of the road. The reduction of the depth of this box from 3 m to 2 m would have significantly reduced the torsional frequency and hence the critical flutter speed. In our opinion the 3 m depth was about right both from the point of view of achieving an adequate flutter speed and also of giving sufficient transverse bending stiffness between the two lines of hangers.

348. **Mr Birdsall** refers to the possible use of spiral strands for the main cables. In addition to the disadvantages which he gives for spiral strands, the difficulty of protecting such a cable from corrosion is made more difficult since the conventional method of wire wrapping and painting is not practical unless the gaps between the outer strands are filled.

349. The modification to BS 153 and HA loading consisted of dividing what was then specified in pounds by 2 and designating them as kilograms, i.e. a lane load of 400 lb/ft. became 200 kg/ft. or an increase of approximately 10%. Mr Birdsall's interpretation of § 52 is correct.

Mr Knox

Many subjects on which I should like to comment from the construction aspect have been raised by several contributors to the discussion so I will group my replies in subject order as in the construction of a suspension bridge.

351. **Mr C. D. Brown** and **Mr Wex** raised the question of steel versus concrete towers. I would accept that in a developed country the first cost of concrete towers is probably less than for steel construction, but they are certainly not quicker. The Humber towers are taking slightly longer than those at Bosporus to build. After this, there is a more significant time disadvantage. Once the last section has been placed on the steel tower the cranes which have erected it can immediately proceed to saddle and footbridge erection. The equipment used for constructing a concrete tower is,

however, quite inadequate for these duties and several weeks are required for installation at the tower top of suitable heavy cranes for the cable and deck phases. Moreover, the provision of attachments in a concrete tower top, suitable in load capacity and accuracy of position for the cranes, footbridge supports, etc., without detracting from construction speed or final appearance, has proved difficult and expensive.

352. **Mr Elliott** asked if availability of steels dictated the uses of different grades in the towers and deck. This is covered in § 335. The grades actually used in Italy, FE52B, 52C and 52D, were all equally available, although, of course, at price differentials.

353. **Mr Dixon** referred to the relaxation of residual shop welding stresses. No dimensional changes due to this were observed on the panels when delivered to site and distortions were minimal. Boltholes between tower components were easily lined up and the very satisfactory speed of deck assembly was not hindered by any 'banana shaped' deck panels.

354. Several speakers referred to the economy of prefabricated parallel wire strands compared to cable spinning. My main comment is that everyone had their chance on this project. Those tendering in competition with us included **Mr Upstone's** company (in a consortium). We were appreciably cheaper than it, not only with our alternative tender for the cable spinning, but also for the conforming design with prefabricated strands. The two examples of the latter which have been built in the world, and other experimental work, have all been done by erection companies which were branches of steel making companies or had wire and cable making companies within the same group; the economic pressures and disciplines which led to the selection of that method may have been rather different from what must apply to an independent fabricating and erecting company such as Cleveland, which must buy in the open market and get guarantees of the product being supplied. In § 90, I referred to the very limited experience with prefabricated parallel wire strands at the time of tender and its limited relevance in scale and success achieved to the cables proposed for Bosporus.

355. The method of constructing the cables of the Otto Beit Bridge, referred to by Sir Ralph Freeman, were an interesting variant for short span suspension bridges, but, as these were formed on site by pulling across ribbons of wire from several single wire coils, this was more properly a form of in situ construction (as cable spinning) rather than off site prefabrication.

356. Very long span suspension bridges employ large cables. For these, cable spinning has increasing advantages over prefabricated strands. On account of manufacturing and handling limitations, the latter will be much smaller than spun strands and many more will be needed to form each cable. This produces greater problems in controlling the partly formed cable, particularly in wind. It also means a much larger number of strand adjustments to be carried out under steady temperature conditions and the smaller strands will require lower wind speeds for satisfactory adjustment than the much heavier spun strands. On most spinning jobs there has been no great trouble spinning the wire at a satisfactory rate, but finding time and suitable conditions for strand adjustment is often much more critical. There is, therefore, unlikely to be any time advantage on a large cable with prefabricated strands. It should be noted that the time taken for the cables of the two bridges so far constructed by the latter method was longer than would have been needed for spinning the same weight of wire. In answer to **Mr Smith**, I do not think that different temperature conditions would affect the decision one way or the other.

357. Availability of equipment was not a factor in the cheaper price for spun cables at Bosporus. The items remaining from the Quebec Bridge were mostly those required for any method of constructing the cables. The particular items for spinning the wire were developed and manufactured new for Bosporus. Clearly with these available, the economic advantage would be even greater.

358. **Mr Birdsall** in § 310 made some comments on the new reeling/unreeling equipment. A further and important factor in achieving the high reeling speeds was the use

DISCUSSION

of light, small capacity reels. These were made possible by the basic idea of combining the reeling and unreeling which obviated the need for removability. Operation of reels of the classic weight at these speeds might cause concern on grounds of safety. Mr Birdsall's deduction of the independent operation of the reels is correct. I regret that § 164 did not make this entirely clear. Routine testing of wire splices was done. This could be reduced to a minimum as the performance of the CCL Systems splice, as developed for the Forth Road Bridge, remained at virtually a zero failure rate.

359. Mr Birdsall raised some queries on the troubles with the tram rope splices. The ropes were 26 mm dia., as has been normal on almost all cable spinning tramways. It seems desirable to limit the length of the splice, as far as is safe, in the interests of minimizing the labour of splicing and reducing the extent of its travel around the far-end turn-around sheaves. Comparative trials on earlier bridges and experiments after the onset of troubles at Bosporus showed no advantage in splices longer than 18 m.

360. The static tension in the tramway rope has to be high enough to ensure that the rope bears against the upper tramway sheaves at each support beam except when the spinning wheel is passing through. The higher the sag ratio or cable stress in the completed bridge, the less curvature exists in the free cable condition and, therefore, the greater the tram rope tension has to be to maintain upper sheave contact.

361. I do not agree with Mr Birdsall that the main cable strand size used was beyond the practicable limit. Despite the problems noted, a satisfactory cable was achieved. The same problems had arisen, to varying degrees, on the Forth and Severn Bridges.

362. The method of spinning the upper strands in the sidespans (back-stays) was criticized by Mr Birdsall. It is correct that wires reversed their vertical position in these strands between the splay point and the tower saddle. This could have been avoided only by spinning the strands in a free catenary from tower saddle to strand shoe. To do so would have resulted in the strand being spun about 2 m high at the bottom of the sidespan, a difficult and possibly dangerous process, and also in unacceptable eccentricity of the line of action of the strand at the strand shoe and its anchor rods. In the event, the additional wire crosses caused by the adopted method did not seem to be deleterious; compacting void ratios in the side spans, even with the unsymmetrical additional backstay strands on top of the cable, were at least as good as in the main span.

363. Mr Birdsall commented further on compacting efficiencies. Strand size alone does not seem to be the main factor, as void ratios with the 548 wire strands at Bosporus were lower than with the 438 wire strands at Severn, despite compacting pressures per wire being lower at Bosporus. On both these bridges, void ratios were greater than at Forth or the North American bridges which he quotes. A possible general conclusion is that 19 strand cables compact less easily than those with 37 or 61 strands.

364. One of Mr Birdsall's most serious criticisms was of the cable band cross section philosophy. I do not think that the differences between the two methods in behaviour of the band castings during bolt tightening are as real as he fears. At Forth, the cable was compacted to an 'ellipse' with the intention of a circular cross-section in the tightened cable bands; at Severn and Bosporus it was compacted to a circle with the expectation of an 'elliptical' cross-section in the bands. Observations and measurement of cable diameters showed that with both procedures there was, during tightening, a distortion of each half of the cable band such that the diameter at the gap face reduced; this reduction was of the same magnitude (4–7 mm) for both types. There seems, therefore, to be a general tendency for the band to 'follow in' the shape as compacted, i.e. an elliptical cable will become a smaller ellipse and a circular cable will tend to remain circular. I think that the predominate factor in this may be the eccentricity of the bolts relative to the circumferential axis of the shell of the casting, allied to the comparative softness of a parallel wire cable. Available data from the year or so that the cable bands have been under observation by the Contractor before completion of the bridges does not indicate any relaxation of this distortion, nor am I aware of any indication that it is in fact harmful to the bands in service. It does, however, create

some practical problems with the bolts, by reducing or eliminating the clearance between their mid-points and the cable and by making the nut bearing faces out of square to their axes, this latter problem not being fully solved by the incorporation of spherical washer faces.

365. I should explain that I use the word 'ellipse' loosely to describe any slightly distorted circle. In many cases, 'oval' or 'combination of segments of a circle' might well be geometrically more correct.

366. I still feel that the benefits of a generally circular cross-section for wrapping are significant. If the cable is compacted with the intention of being circular in the final cable bands, the difference between the two diameters, as generally compacted and as presented for wrapping, will be 20–25 mm on most cables. If the wrapping machine has fingers, which I consider essential for tight wrapping, their radial movement must provide for half of this difference as well as that caused by the unavoidable residual and varying lack of concentricity of the cable and machine axes. In practice this proved difficult at Forth without excessive variation of the finger spring pressure or even by reaching the limits of its available movement. With the circular cable at Severn and Bosporus this problem was greatly reduced.

367. I should like to endorse **Mr Blakeley**'s remarks on the specified method of tightening the cable band bolts. A study of the records of bolt extension measurements shows that there was much more uncertainty about the actual loads left in individual bolts at Bosporus than at Severn where the final stretching beyond the proportional limit was not done until the final round of tightening just before completion of the bridge. The conventional method of avoiding any tightening beyond the elastic range, of course, gives almost complete certainty of final bolt loads. There seems also no doubt, from experience at Forth and Bosporus, that normal thread forms cannot withstand repeated tightening to almost the ultimate stress of the bolts without significant thread damage.

368. **Mr Hyatt** and **Mr Smith** commented on the fact that there were no tenders for the alternative truss-stiffened design. Although my company decided at the time of tender not to make an estimate for this, I have since considered that it might have been worth doing so. In particular, for an overseas project there would have been several savings over the box deck design. Shipping damage to the truss members would have been much less than for the stiffened plate panels; the technical, labour and painting problems caused by the assembly and transverse joint welding would have been eliminated; the assembly area could have been much smaller and simpler; the times for assembly and final connexion of the sections would have been much reduced. Whether these savings would have countered the additional quantities of some materials and of the substructure work would need full comparative estimating, based on the experience we now have, to determine.

369. In answer to Mr Smith, I believe that the New Elizabeth Bridge at Budapest (300 m span), and the Emmerich Bridge (500 m span) incorporate the orthotropic steel deck as part of the top chord of the stiffening truss.

370. Mr Birdsall drew attention to the apparent contradiction between my remarks and those of the Authors of Part I regarding tolerances in the components of the box deck. I can only reiterate that the Contractor's experience on Severn and Bosporus, and currently at Humber, has shown that the work of assembling satisfactory box sections is made much more difficult, slow and costly if the individual panels are not manufactured within at least the tolerances specified by the Contractor for Bosporus. The problem arises from the large number of panels making up the cross-section with consequent magnification of any discrepancies. With 13 seams across the deck width, even the 2 mm range of panel widths worked to for Bosporus can cause a variation of up to 26 mm in total width. It should be noted that normal fabrication practice, if tolerances are not laid down and enforced, is likely to produce greater errors on such stiffened plate construction. The results of inaccuracy show in diaphragm connexions not lining up, in varying and incorrect roadway levels and cross-falls, and in complete

DISCUSSION

box sections becoming out of square; tedious corrective measures, including cutting and repreparation of plate edges, repeated removal and reinsertion of panels and ad hoc methods of levelling the deck, are then needed. Setting the panels to individually determined gaps rather than the desired tight butt condition is not a satisfactory answer; this is time-consuming, prone to further error, and increases weld shrinkage, which is technically undesirable and leads to further unpredictable errors in dimension. The site costs caused by these problems, including the effects of delays, are appreciably greater than the cost of ensuring adequate shop accuracy.

371. **Mr Upstone**'s remarks about the backing strip system for the deck welds were largely answered by later speakers. I am confident that gaps, as shown in his diagrams, did not apply at Bosporus and do not at Humber. Those who have been closely involved in using the system have, in fact, commented that its features result in the backing strip being pulled up very tightly to the plates as the welding takes place.

372. Mr Upstone and Mr Smith advocated thinner types of surfacing, probably based on epoxy resins. Several other speakers drew attention to the reduction of deck fatigue life which this would cause. Over the last ten years, my company has been involved on several bridges, mostly moveable or temporary, which had thin epoxy coatings of varying specification, manufacturer and applicator. Some were proposed by us. All have failed, and we do not now consider that this method should be pursued any further. The thick coatings (6–8 cm) of the bituminous asphalt type have been laid, partly or wholly, by machine on several bridges in other European countries; these have apparently been successful and I think that the future must lie in this direction. In reply to Mr Smith, steel decks alone can be made flat enough for road traffic; the measured riding quality of Severn was better before surfacing than after. Skid resistance would, however, be a problem, as would the fatigue life mentioned by other speakers.

373. I should like to conclude by expressing my appreciation of the keen interest shown in the Paper and of the many constructive points brought out in the discussion.

References

7. OSTENFELDT C. and JOHNSON W. *Suspension bridge across Lillebaelt*. Copenhagen, 1970.
8. BIRDSALL B., *et al*. Discussion and Closure on Scalzi and McGrath, Mechanical properties of structural cables. *J. Struct. Div., ASCE*, 1972, **98** ST8, Aug. 1883; 1973, **99** ST4, April, 790.
9. YAM L. C. P. and MOTT H. G. B. C. *Tenth scale models for stiffened flanges of steel box girders*. Lab. Rep. 664. Transport and Road Research Laboratory, Crowthorne, 1975.
10. HORNE M. R. and NARAYANAN R. Ultimate capacity of longitudinally stiffened plates used in box girders. *Proc. Instn Civ. Engrs*, Part 2, 1976, **61**, June, 253–280.